REA

THE GOLDEN TALISMAN
AND
THE ANCIENT
ALPHABET

By
Robert A. Logan

DORRANCE & COMPANY, INCORPORATED
828 LANCASTER AVENUE • BRYN MAWR, PENNSYLVANIA 19010
Publishers Since 1920

CONTENTS

1
A TALISMAN SAVES
A LIFE

"How can this be! How could it be possible that this man from a far distant country was carrying a metal copy of the missing half of our most sacred and most treasured relic of our ancestors—the Golden Talisman? This is very strange, indeed! There must be more to it than meets the eye. We must do our best to keep him alive so that he may tell us what he knows of the mystery!

"Truly," he added, more to himself than to his companions, "my daughter was right. There must be some mysterious connection between this man and the early people of our ancient race."

The speaker, a tall elderly North American Indian, was gazing with awe and reverence at a small metal plate that by some miracle had deflected an arrow that, but for it, would have pierced the heart of the unconscious man on the ground before him.

An hour earlier the scene had been very different.

The fragrance-laden afternoon air was warm, without a trace of breeze to flutter the leaves of the tall cottonwood trees along the bank of the stream in which two large birchbark canoes were being paddled steadily against the sluggish current of the northward flowing waters of the stream then known in the Indian language of the paddlers as Mih-kwa-kum-me-wee See-pee—the Red Water River; which some two hundred years later would be better known as the Red River of the North forming part of the boundary between the states of Minnesota and North Dakota and flowing into the Canadian province of Manitoba.

On this sultry afternoon, from a cloudless sky, the August sun poured its hot rays upon the glistening backs of four Indian paddlers in each canoe. They had been working their way upstream from the junction of the main river and a river flowing into it from the west; a place that some two hundred years later would be known as the site of the city of Winnipeg.

After six days of strenuous labor at the paddles, they were now some one hundred and thirty miles from their starting point, and in land that many, many moons later would be known as the States of Minnesota and Dakota but which, then, was wild land vaguely claimed by "The Company of Adventurers of England Trading into Hudson's Bay" by virtue of their Royal Charter which gave them practically imperial control over all land having waters draining into Hudson's Bay.

In the center part of each canoe sat a man. One appeared to be merely a passenger while the other was apparently the captain of the little flotilla, as he kept peering ahead and from time to time spoke to the paddlers as if he were giving them directions. He was dressed in Indian garb, and from the respectful attention given to him by the paddlers it was evident that he was either a chief or a medicine man.

The passenger, although showing a face tanned almost as brown as the skin of his companions, was obviously a white man. He wore an Indian style buckskin shirt or jacket, but his head-dress was that of the white men of his time, and below this could be seen hair that was decidedly reddish in color instead of the straight black hair of his companions.

He was seated slightly more comfortably than were the kneeling paddlers. The relatively light birchbark canoes were easy to upset unless all weight was kept as low as possible. All paddlers kneeled and all passengers were required to sit as close as possible to the bottom of the canoe. No one would think of sitting on a crossbar or thwart of such a water-craft.

While being paddled southward the passenger was trying to write in a notebook on his knee, but the bright sunshine reflected from the paper was bothering him. Looking ahead, he could see a slight bend in the western bank of the river where tall trees close to the shore cast a shadow over a fairly quiet section of the water. He called to the captain of the other canoe, who directed his paddlers to move closer to the white man, who then spoke to the captain in the Indian language.

"What do you think," he said, "about letting the men have a few minutes rest in the shade of the trees when we reach that shadowed spot? While they are resting out of the hot sun I could write some notes without being blinded by the glare from the paper. If you

2

agree with me and could tell your men to take a short rest in the shade of the trees I would appreciate it."

"Certainly, my friend," replied the Indian captain. "I think we are reasonably safe from any enemy attack here, although resting in a spot so close to the trees and underbrush on a river bank is rather against my training and experience in traveling outside tribal territory."

The men with the paddles were told to rest their arms and to let the canoes float at a distance of about fifty paces from the water's edge. All was quiet in a few moments and the white man began to write.

He had just written at the head of a fresh page the day's date, "17 August 1725 A.D.," and the words "Proceeding nearly due south upstream on the Red Water River flowing into the great 'Lake of Dirty Water' in south western Prince Rupert's Land" when his thoughts were interrupted by a request from one of the paddlers in his canoe to be allowed to go ashore for a few minutes. Without thinking, the white man said, "Sure, go ahead," and the canoe was almost touching land before he realized that he was not in command, as was the usual case with him, and that he should first have spoken to the captain of the flotilla about letting his canoe men pull to the river bank. By that time, however, it was too late.

No sooner had two men jumped ashore when they were met by wild war whoops and a shower of arrows and scattered musket shots from Indians who sprang from the shelter of the shrubbery under the trees.

The main target of the assault seemed to be the white man. His right leg and left arm were both broken by bullets. An arrow passed through the fleshy part of his left thigh and another arrow would have pierced his heart had it not been deflected by a small metal plate—a talisman of bronze—suspended by a leather thong hanging around his neck. Another bullet creased the side of his head and he slumped unconscious to the bottom of the canoe.

The paddlers in the other canoe had not been disabled, as they were farther out in the stream. They quickly grabbed their muskets and fired at the enemy, with much shouting.

Suddenly, the fighting stopped almost as surprisingly as it had begun. When the captain in the other canoe shouted to his men near the stricken canoe a tall Indian came out of the shrubbery on

3

the river bank and shouted to his men to cease the attack and called to the captain of the canoe flotilla. He addressed him by name and asked him to cease fire because the attack on the canoes was all a mistake—a case of mistaken identity.

The leader of the men on the land and the leader of the men of the canoes were old acquaintances although of different Indian nations. The canoe men were of the nation known to themselves as the Nay-he-yaw-wayoo people, and generally called by their neighbours Knistinoos or Kilistinoos. (Much later they were known to the white men by the shorter name, "Crees.")

The men on the land were of the Dakota nation (later given the name Sioux by the French). The chief of the Dakotas explained that they thought the canoe men were Ojibways (or Chippewas), and that the white man was a Frenchman, because it was not usual for Cree men to travel so far south, and also because they had heard that a Frenchman was on his way to spy out the land of the Dakotas, and they were trying to prevent him from doing so.

As quickly as possible both sides began to bind up their wounds. Both friends and late enemies helped to move the wounded and unconscious white man to a quickly made bed of bunched together balsam branches on the shore. The captain of the canoe flotilla proved to be a renowned medicine man and, of course, he took charge.

The white man's clothing was removed after the shaft of the arrow through his thigh had been broken and pulled out of the bleeding flesh. To the surprise of all, it was found that a metal plate of some kind, worn by the white man, although badly dented, had prevented an arrow from hitting his heart.

At first, no particular attention was paid to the metal plate because all attention was being given to stopping the flow of blood from the big white man's several wounds, but when the bleeding had been fairly successfully stopped and all attempts to have him return to consciousness had failed, the medicine man washed the metal plate and examined it carefully. He was very, very much astonished by what he found.

He found the metal to be of a nature not seen by him before this time. He was familiar with metals introduced by the white men—steel, iron, silver, gold, lead and copper, as well as some native copper to be found in places along the southern shore of the great lake

4

known as Kitshe Kumee—but this was a brownish metal; stiff but soft enough to have had markings cut or engraved upon it.

As he examined the markings on the metal he was still more astonished to find that they were markings well known to him but believed by him to exist on only one piece of metal—a plate of solid gold—respected as one of the most ancient sacred relics of his own ancient ancestors. How could such a thing be in the possession of a white man! Here was mystery, indeed!

He wrapped the plate carefully in dried grass and buckskin and said to his companions, "This strange metal plate has saved the life of our white friend so I must now carefully guard it for him—for truly it must be something serving the will of the Great Spirit."

"Now," he said emphatically, "let us return as quickly as possible to our summer camping ground, where I will try to repair the damage done to our friend Mis-see-nay-kaw—'Big Sandy.' "

2
GIRL MEETS MAN

When the man known to the Indians as "Big Sandy" awoke, at long last, his mind was reasonably clear once more but he had no idea where he was. His memory was a blank from the time when he heard the first wild cries of the attacking Indians on the shore of the river.

He could barely move anything except his eyes and his right hand. He could see that he was not in a canoe or in the forest. Slowly he realized that he was in an Indian lodge or teepee and that near him was a girl, about seventeen years of age, dressed in the garments worn by American Indian women in that year of 1725 A.D., but her face was almost as white as that of a tanned European woman, and a thing that amazed him was the color of her long hair. Instead of the straight jet black hair of all Indian women he had seen, the hair of this girl was wavy and was definitely reddish brown.

She looked so much like many of the women of the Scottish highlands, where he had been born, that instinctively he spoke to her in his mother tongue, the Gaelic of Scotland, asking, "Where am I?" and "Who are you?"

When the girl seemed unable to understand his questions, he asked again, in English: "Where am I and who are you?" Again he could see only complete mystification on the face of the girl, so he repeated the questions in the Indian tongue: *"Tan itay ka ayan?"* *"Aweenu keenu?"* "Where is it that I am?" "Who art thou?"

At once her face lit up and she answered with a smile, "Thou art in the lodge of my father, Kee-see-pay-pim-moo-tay-oo, Chief Medicine Man. I am his youngest daughter, Pah-peet-tshah-koos, 'Laughing Star', called 'Papeet' by my friends.

"I have been told to sit beside thee and as soon as thou becamest awake to call my father. I shall call him at once."

Tshaskwa! Tshaskwa! Wait! Wait!" said the white man urgently. "Tell me, are you a white woman held captive by the Indians?"

6

She looked at him indignantly for a moment but, seeing the sincere look on his face, her sudden show of anger turned to amusement as she said, "Certainly I am not a white woman held captive by the Indians. I am an Indian. I am the daughter of my honorable father, the Chief Medicine Man of the Lake Winnepik Nay-he-ya-way-oo people. What makes you think I might be a white woman?"

"Your hair is not like that of any Indian woman I have ever seen. You look almost like my own sister, about your age, back on the Isle of Skye. That is why I spoke to you first in my own native language." He added earnestly, "I can not understand the resemblance. It is almost as if you and I were blood relatives, in spite of the facts that a wide, wide ocean lies between the lands of your birth and mine. Somewhere in the long, long ago some of our ancestors must have been of the same people."

"Strange, indeed," admitted the girl softly, "but that is exactly the idea that entered my head when I first saw you, on the day you arrived here from the north."

"From the north!" exclaimed the man. "Then why did I not see you before this?"

"Because," admitted the girl shyly, "I kept out of your sight. But I was very interested in you and I asked many questions of all those who saw or talked with you. I asked my friends to find out all they could about you from your companions."

"You did, eh!" chuckled the man on the bed. "And did you learn about my wife and children back at The Bay?"

"I learned," said the girl with a sound of satisfaction in her voice, "that you are known to have had no wife and, unlike many white men in our country, there are no children who can call you 'father' since you first came to our land five years ago."

"And were you disappointed to learn that?" teased the man.

A blush spread over the face of the girl as she dropped her eyes and admitted softly, "I was not disappointed." Then, trying to recover her composure, she added quickly, "I must call my father. He will be glad to know that you have awakened at last."

The medicine man had been sitting with the Chief at some distance so that their voices would not disturb the sleeping man. At his daughter's call, he entered the tent, accompanied by the Chief. Both men expressed their happiness that the white man had recovered consciousness and was able to talk with them.

They told him how sorry they were that such a misfortune had befallen him and they hoped that he would not blame them for what had happened. They told him that although his visit to them had brought misfortune to himself they were sure that his visit had brought good fortune to them as a group. Several of their young men and three of his canoe men had gone on a buffalo hunt, a day's journey to the westward, and had surprised a herd of fat animals. They had killed so many that all the women in the encampment would be busy for many days drying the meat and making pemmican. The Chief told Sandy that a buffalo steak was already sizzling for the meal they hoped he would be able to eat.

"I am very grateful to you for what you have done for me, and, of course, I do not blame you for what happened," said the man on the bed, and he added, with a smile, "Right now I feel hungry enough to eat a whole buffalo. But tell me, please, how did I get here and how long have I been out of my head? The last I remember was being in a canoe when we were attacked by Indians on the shore of the river."

"You were brought down the river in two nights and a day," the Chief told him, "and you have been here, at the fork of the Red River[1] for three nights and two days before this day. All that time, you were either asleep or talking at random as men do when delirious."

"Did I do much talking?" the big man asked.

"Yes," he was told. "But you talked in several languages unknown to us. One of your men told us that he recognized words of the language spoken by white men at The Bay but the words did not make much sense to him. Another of your men recognized some words of the language spoken by the white men from Kawapek, but most of your talking seemed to be in a language unknown to any of us."

"That language," said the wounded man, with a smile, "was probably my mother tongue, the language I learned at my mother's knee on the far away misty island of the Inner Hebrides."

"But are you not an Englishman?" asked the Chief in surprise.

"No," said the big man, "I am not an Englishman, although I do work for an English company. I am a Scottish Highlander from the Isle of Skye, many miles north of the land of the Englishmen. My first language is Gaelic; my second language is English, and my

8

third language is French, in which I am not expert, but my fourth language and the one I like best of all, although I still have much to learn about it, is the language you speak—*Nay-he-yaw-way-win.*"

He continued: "For several years I was a mariner and navigator of ships sailing back and forth across the great salt ocean between Old England and New England, the land of the 'Boston-men.' Then I came to your great country and spent some time exploring and mapping the country for the English fur trading company of Hudson's Bay.[2] At first, I made maps of the Bay and the country close to it, traveling by water in summer and by snowshoe and dogtrain in winter. For the past two summers I have been exploring rivers between the salt water of The Bay and Kitshe Kumee, the great fresh water lake to the east of us. This year I hoped to explore a part of this country, and next year, I hope to explore the country to the west of Lake Winnepik."

"I am afraid, my friend," said the Chief, "that your traveling is ended for the next several months. Before you can be sufficiently recovered from your wounds to make portages, the cold weather will be here. You can not return to the salt water now, in your condition, but we cordially invite you to winter with us at our winter hunting grounds on the eastern shore of Lake Winnepik, where our friend the medicine man will be able to patch up your wounds and get you in condition to travel again when the streams are free of ice next spring."

He turned to the medicine man, saying, "Is that what you recommend?"

"Indeed it is what I recommend," said the medicine man, and, turning to the white man, he continued: "I led you into the ambush that gave you your wounds and I wish to do my best to make you whole and strong again. For that reason I invite you to share my dwelling while you are with us. When I lost my only son, my older daughter was already married to the chief of a neighboring band of our people, so, therefore, my younger daughter, Papeetshakoos, became my heir and successor as a medicine woman and she has been trained in all my arts and skills. She will be my assistant in getting you back on your feet again."

"I thank you," said the white man. "I am sure I could not wish for a better doctor—or nurse. Your invitation is a great temptation."

9

"I must admit, however," said the medicine man, "that I have another motive for wishing to have your companionship for a while. In fact, I have more than one motive. You are a widely traveled man and I am keenly interested in learning about other lands, other peoples, and other customs; but, more than that, I wish to learn from you something of the mystery of the metal plate that you were wearing when you were hit by that Dakota arrow. But, my friend, we must not tire you out by talking now. We shall have time for that later. We will leave you now in the care of your nurse. Try to sleep as much as you can. Try to forget about your troubles. Just rest and let your broken bones grow together and let your flesh wounds heal."

As the men left him, the girl entered carrying a slab of buffalo steak on a plate of wood and a small birchbark dish containing boiled wild rice.

Sandy started to speak to her but she shook her head as she signaled to him to eat. She propped up his head and began feeding him, bite by bite. When he had eaten and his head was lowered onto his pillow, he tried to sleep but, for a while, he had too much to think about, to permit sleep: Here he was, hundreds of weary miles from his base and not likely to be able to travel for months to come. He had six men who must be sent back to The Bay with his report of work done since they started out in the spring, and he still had part of that report to write. While trying to compose the latter he finally dropped off to sleep.

When he awoke it was dark. He could hear the breathing of at least two other people in the lodge. He started to move his good arm but instantly a gentle hand touched his shoulder and the soft voice of the girl whispered, "Are you all right? That is my father you hear snoring—and my mother is there too," she added.

He chuckled almost silently and said, "Yes, I am all right, so long as my *Powakun*—my dream spirit—is here beside me." He reached out his hand and met hers and was still holding it when he went to sleep again.

When he woke it was daylight; the dogs were barking, the people of the encampment were stirring, and he was alone in the lodge.

During the next several days he held many talks with the Chief, the medicine man and others of the band, as well as with his chief canoe man whom he now delegated to take charge of the others of their party.

Of necessity, these talks were of short duration at first, but each day, as his strength came back, the periods of talking became longer, and his one good arm, fortunately his right arm, was soon kept busy writing his reports.

The big white man told his Indian friends that the name they could call him was "Santee"; not Mis-see-nay-kaw as he had been called by the Bay Indians who had accompanied him to the Red River. He explained that the name Mis-see-nay-kaw was a Bay Indian interpretation of the name by which he was known among the white men of the Bay. To the white men he was known as "Big Sandy." The "Sandy" part of his name, so he told them, had really nothing to do with sand, *nay-kaw*, but was a "short name" for his official name, "Alexander"—his full name being Alexander Mac-Donald. The Indian attempts to pronounce the English word "Sandy" resulted in something more like the sound of San-Tee, because the sound of the English letter "D" was almost unknown in this Indian tongue.

It was settled that he would spend the winter with the band at their winter encampment and that his Bay Indians would return home and come back for him in the spring when the streams were clear of ice.

It was arranged that three hundred pounds of prime pemmican would be carried back to the Company's headquarters on the Bay. This would be in addition to ample supplies to be used by the canoe men en route home. The Lake Winnepik Indians were paid for this by presents of a trade—gun and ammunition to the Chief; two copper cooking-pots and a hunting knife to the medicine man; and, to various members of the band, a variety of small presents from the stock of trade goods carried by the party from the Bay. The Indians were very well satisfied with the exchange and promised not to trade their next winter's catch of fur until the canoe men returned from the Bay, in the following spring.

3
SANDY REPORTS
TO HIS CHIEF

Soon the wounded man, aided by his ever attentive nurse, was able
to write the last chapter of his report to his employers, as follows:

. . . On the seventeenth day of August of this year 1725 A.D., I
was in one of two canoes being paddled almost due southward up
the stream known to the Indians as Mih-kwa-kum-me-wee Seepee—the Red (water) River—so called because of the reddish mud
along its banks and because of the reddish color of the water during
the spring floods. The occupants of the canoes, with the exception
of myself, were Indians of the NAYHEYAWAYOO Nation (or K'NIS-
TINEAUX as they are called by the French).

The members of this particular band of Indians live during the
summer at the confluence of the Red River and a stream flowing
into it from the west. At this place, the Indians are able to hunt
buffalo that roam the plains to the westward, but during the long,
cold, and windy winters they live about a week's canoe journey to
the northward on the wooded eastern side of the great lake that
extends north and south for two or three hundred miles (according
to my informants).

The discolored waters of the Red River, which flows into the
southern extremity of this body of water, have helped to give the
latter the name "Lake Winnepik." I translate this as "Lake of the
Dirty Water."

We had arrived a few days earlier at the Indian summer camp at
the fork of the Red River, and had been cordially welcomed by the
local chief after I explained to him that I was an explorer and map
maker for the English company of traders on the Hudson's Bay.

The Indians, who had accompanied me from the Bay southwestward across the watershed between the streams running into the
bay and the streams running into Lake Winnepik, speak the lan-

12

guage of the Indians we found on the Red River, but with slight dialectical differences that do not seriously interfere with the understanding of what is being said by either group. Fortunately, I am fluent in the language of the Bay Indians and have no difficulty in conversing with these Winnepik Indians.

After my arrival at the fork of the Red River, I held long talks with the chief, and others of his band, endeavoring to learn about the unknown country to the west, north, and south. At most of these talks we were joined by several of his councilors, including the Chief Medicine Man, a tall, very intelligent appearing man about forty-nine years of age, who is known to the other Indians by the name KEE-SEE-PAY-PIM-MOO-TAY-OO—"He has finished walking about"—a name or title given to him because of his extensive travels before he settled down as "Chief Medicine Man."

I arranged with the Chief for several of his men to work with me for a few days to replace my canoe men in order that the latter might have some rest after their laborious journey from the Bay to the Red River. It was intended that the River Indians would paddle up the Red River—to the south—as far as they could go in three days. We would then return to the Indian encampment at the fork of the river and would then go up the stream that flows from the west. It was thought that after about ten days it would be necessary for my party to begin the return journey to the fort on the Bay.

On my exploration of the two rivers, I was to be accompanied, as guide, by the medicine man, KEE-SEE-PAY-PIM-MOO-TAY-OO— whose name I shall reduce to KESEE PAY when referring to him in writing—who is an expert canoe man and experienced traveler, famed for having traveled far and wide as a wandering diplomat and story teller and medicine man, ever seeking information that might increase his skill as a sorcerer, juggler and general medicine man. He has learned several languages other than his own, and has exchanged ideas with the wisest men of several neighboring Indian nations. He is still a great seeker after knowledge, and quite apparently was delighted to have the opportunity to spend a few days in close association with a white man with whom he could converse easily, and from whom he hoped to learn much.

On the afternoon of the third day of the journey southward from the Indian encampment, we were about to make camp when we were surprised by a volley of gunfire and a shower of arrows from a party of Dakota Indians. In the ensuing fight three of the canoe men and myself were badly wounded, and probably the whole party would have been killed except for a very surprising development. The leader of the Dakotas suddenly recognized the medicine man KESEE PAY as an old friend and called off the fight althought his men outnumbered our canoe men by about five to one.

Nobody on either side had been killed but several men on each side had wounds to show—and later to brag about when they would describe, and magnify, the terrible battle in which they had taken part. Unfortunately, the most severely wounded man was myself. KESEE PAY told me later that the Dakotas explained to him that they thought I was a Frenchman and that the Indians with me were Chippewas from the Kitshe Kumee[3] country to the eastward with whom they were at war.

I had been the main target and my right leg and left arm were both broken by bullets. An arrow had passed through the fleshy part of the thigh of my left leg and an arrow might have pierced my heart had it not been deflected by a small metal plate which I carried on a thong around my neck.

The medicine man attended to my wounds and in the course of this discovered the metal plate which I carried. This discovery greatly excited the Indian and as soon as I was sufficiently recovered from the shock and pain of my wounds to be able to talk, the first question put to me by the medicine man was:

"Can my friend from the salt water lake tell me why he carries this metal plate?"

"I carry it because it was given to me by an Indian friend several years ago," I answered truthfully. "My friend claimed that it would bring me luck and protect me from violent death."

"It has indeed protected you to the extent of saving your life, at least," said the medicine man, "but whether it has brought you luck seems to be another matter. It is a strange kind of luck that brings you such serious wounds, but if it had not been for the plate, an arrowhead would have entered your heart. But tell me," he added earnestly, "do you know the meanings of the markings on the plate?"

"No," I told him truthfully. "I know a little something of a story about the plate but I know nothing of the meanings of the markings. I was told by my Indian friend that the markings were copied

14

from a very old gold plate formerly in the possession of a red-haired stranger who visited the Indians shortly before the great fire, thousands of miles from this place, and many thousands of years ago."

Since that time, I have had many talks with the local Indians and I feel that I am in good hands as far as recovery of my wounds is concerned. As it is obvious that I can not attempt to return to the Bay before freeze-up, I have accepted the invitation to spend the winter with these Indians at their winter quarters on the eastern side of Lake Winnepik, near the mouth of the river known to the Indians by the name ETOMAMEE SEEPEE, about one hundred and thirty miles from the southern end of Lake Winnepik. I estimate this to be located at about fifty-two degrees north latitude and about ninety-seven degrees west longitude. I have been told that on the opposite side of the great lake, but some fifty miles farther north, there is a river entering the lake, and that it drains the waters from a series of large lakes and streams and provides a transportation route roughly parallel to, but south of, the water route via the MISSENEPEE RIVER and which is the route followed by interior Indians of the NAYHEYAWAYOO Nation who trade at our station, KITSHEWASKUHIKUN on the Bay. I think this potential route should be explored and I would like to do that in the summer of 1726, assuming, of course, that I am not recalled by you. I assume that orders will be sent to me at ETOMAMEE SEEPEE as soon as navigation of the rivers and lakes is possible when they open in the spring.

If I spend next summer continuing the exploration of this region, it will be necessary for you to send to me the almanac of sun and moon positions for the year 1726, which, I assume, was received from London during the summer. I also require a small bottle of quicksilver for my artificial horizon. My supply of this was lost in our battle with the Dakota Indians.

I have been told by my nurse—the medicine man's daughter, who, like her father, is an exceptionally intelligent person—that I should be able to make observations for double altitudes of celestial objects by means of a dish of thick maple syrup, made by diluting with water the sugar which the Indians make from the sap of maple trees in the spring. I shall try out the idea as soon as I am back on my feet and, if it is workable, I may be able to determine some geographic positions during the winter.

I believe that my enforced stay with these friendly Indians will be useful both to the Company and to me. It will provide a good opportunity to establish friendly relations with the Indians of this region, and the regions to the west and south, and to encourage them to increase their fur catch and to trade with the Company. I shall be able to collect reports from many Indians who have ranged widely over the country to the west. It will also give me a good opportunity to perfect myself in the dialect of these Indians, as I have been told that it is the chief dialect spoken in the country to the west of Lake Winnepik.

It closely resembles the dialects of the Bay Indians but to speak it properly one must know where and when to substitute other sounds for the "L" sounds and some of the "N" sounds of the dialects spoken nearer the salt water, (and also where to substitute "K" sounds for some of the "TSH" sounds of the dialect spoken on the eastern side of the Bay). This dialect has no sounds of "L" or "R", and few sounds of "SH," except the frequent use of "TSH." The sounds of "SH" of the Bay dialects is generally replaced by the sound of "S" alone. Without experience in hearing the words spoken with these changes it is at times difficult to follow what may be said, if words are spoken rapidly.

This is a very important matter when listening to descriptions of places given by the Indians. My friend, the local medicine man, has told me that *this* dialect is actually the old language of their ancestors who lived many centuries ago somewhere to the southwest of this country in a land now all under water. He claims that he has proof of the older civilization and that he will explain it to me later. He seems to think that I am mixed up with some mystery about the written language of that ancient civilization because of the strange markings on the metal plate which saved my life recently.

I do not understand just what it is all about, but hope to know before I hear from you in the spring. In the meantime, I shall endeavor to compile a list of words and phrases of the Indian language for the use of Company employees. For that, fortunately, I am well supplied with paper and ink.

Sandy MacDonald also wrote a letter to the officer in command of the Company's main establishment on Hudson's Bay, a man he looked upon as a personal friend as well as being his superior officer.

He addressed this as "Personal and Confidential" and included the following:

As you know, my original 'Articles of Agreement' for service with the Honourable Company is due to expire next summer and it was expected, when I left the fort, that before I returned there this autumn you would have received a reply from London as to whether the agreement would be renewed, for a like period of time, or whether our association would be terminated and I should return to Britain on the supply ship leaving the Bay in the summer of 1726.

I had offered to continue with the Company and you had been kind enough to recomment that I be re-engaged, particularly to continue the exploring, surveying and map-making work in which you are so interested, but what neither of us could know is whether the gentlemen in London would agree either to my continued association with you or to your proposals for more extensive exploration of the interior of this vast country.

I shall have to await your reply when the canoe men come back in the spring. If it has been decided that I must return to Britain, I shall immediately proceed to the Bay in order to sail on the ship next summer; but if, as I hope, it has been decided that I remain in America to continue explorations, I respectfully suggest that you send me equipment and supplies to enable me to engage Indians from Lake Winnepik to workwith me during the coming summer and the following winter and part of the following summer, so that I would return to the Bay at the end of the summer of 1727.

I believe that there are wonderful opportunities to increase the fur trade in the interior of the country, but first we must find the best routes for the movement of supplies and trade goods into the interior, and for the movement of furs down to the salt water. From what I have heard of activities of the French from Canada in the regions to the south of the great lakes, it may not be long before they may attempt to trade with "our" Indians of the interior if we do not begin to carry our trade to those Indians.

There is one matter on which I do crave your counsel and advice. If I should continue to work in this country after next summer, I may wish to marry. Would there be any serious objections on the part of the Company if I should bring back to the fort a wife? Would I be able to live within the fort and draw Company rations for her? At this moment these are more or less theoretical questions, but I have a peculiar feeling—perhaps a touch of 'Highland second

17

sight'—that by the time your answers to these questions arrive here, they may possibly be of great importance to me. Therefore, I respectfully ask that you advise me without fail.

I have the honour to be, Sir,
Your humble and obedient servant,
Alexander MacDonald

4
SANDY AND THE
MEDICINE MAN

The canoe men from the Bay began their return journey on the first day of September. They intended to retrace the route they had followed to the Red River.

After their departure, half a moon went by while the Indians on the river killed more buffalo and made more pemmican. The meaty parts of the buffalo were cut into thin slices and hung on racks to dry in the sun and over smoke-fires. When sufficiently dry and hard, these slices of meat were pounded to powder and put into sacks made of the skin of the animals. Sometimes the dried and powdered meat was mixed with dried berries. Sometimes a little maple sugar was added. The powdered mixture in the skin bags was covered with melted buffalo fat and the bags were securely tied to keep out air or dampness. The resulting material, called pemmican, could be kept for many months—even for years—and was highly concentrated food. A small quantity of it could provide nourishment for many hours. Sometimes it was eaten dry, sometimes mixed with boiled roots, and sometimes made into a stew with wild rice or other seeds, or berries.

With the Indians, one unit of time was a "moon"—from the time of first sighting of a new moon until the next new moon. Each "moon" had a name associated with some feature of nature. This particular moon was known as "The moon when animals chase each other." This had reference to the rutting season of the horned animals, such as deer, moose, caribou, etc.

On the day before the full moon, the Indians began their journey northward to their winter hunting grounds, where there were more forests and not such bitter winter winds as those that blew from the great plains, to the westward of the encampment on the Red River.

The wound in the white man's thigh was healing satisfactorily, but his arm and his other leg were tied up in splints and any movement was painful. His friends, the Indians, carried him on a stretcher and placed him in the largest canoe where he was fairly comfortable except one day when the wind on the big lake made such choppy waves that it was necessary to go ashore for the best part of the day and to travel by moonlight after the wind of the afternoon turned to the calm of the evening.

At last, the flotilla arrived at its destination, to be greeted by wild howling of dogs that had been left to rustle for themselves during the summer. The camp was soon reestablished and preparations were made for the winter routine; for the next moon would bring cold weather and probably snow.

At every opportunity the white man listened carefully to, and practiced the pronunciation of, the words of the Indian language according to the dialect of the people with whom he found himself. He was told that a working knowledge of this dialect would enable him to converse with, and to understand, Indians all across the northern plains country from Lake Winnepik to the great mountains of rock on the western side of the plains. For his purposes of exploration it was essential that he be able to converse understandingly with informants directly, without having to depend on interpreters.

He learned that there was another large lake lying roughly parallel to the great "lake of dirty water" or Lake Winnepik. He was told of the route that could be followed to reach the lake and how to ascend a river flowing into its northwesterly end and thus to find another large lake into which flowed streams from the great country to the west. He was told of the great river to the north of these lakes that had its source in the mountains of rock and flowed easterly and northeasterly to its outlet into the northern part of Lake Winnepik. Because of sections of rapidly flowing water this river was known as the Kisiskatshewan.[4]

And far to the north of this river, so he was told, was still another river or chain of lakes known as the Missenepee or "Great Water," which flowed easterly into the great Salt Water. This latter stream he recognized as the waterway flowing into Hudson's Bay at about fifty-nine degrees north latitude.

The more he listened to reports of the country to the westward the more interested he became and the more determined to be the first English-speaking person to explore it and to record such explorations on accurate maps. He was told that a few French-speaking men had traveled westward into the country and a few of them had returned, but little was known of what they may have seen or reported about their explorations.

It was fortunate that he had brought with him many books of blank paper in which to write the results of his conversations with the Indians. He was surprised to find the Indians to be so highly intelligent and so well informed about many things, both physical and mental. When he arrived in the land of the Indians on the Bay, he had been told, by people who thought they knew, that the Indians had no idea of abstract things or abstract ideas and could understand and talk about only those things they could see or feel. He had soon found reason to doubt that description of the mental capabilities of the Indians, and after he became fluent in their language he realized that the reason why the white men thought the Indians had no words or idioms for abstract ideas was simply ignorance on the part of the white men—ignorance of the whole idea of the idioms, structure and usage of the Indian language, in which idea sequences were almost the reverse of those of the European languages of his time.

Not only did these inland Indians know much about the white settlements along the Atlantic seaboard, but they knew quite a lot about the Spaniards in Mexico, and they had many traditions about prehistoric civilizations in North America.

He found that the medicine man, far from being an ignorant savage, knew more about some subjects than he did himself, although he was admittedly ignorant about many customs of white men of the time and about many things that were considered to be simple facts of common knowledge to the average "civilized" white man.

In the day-to-day life in the home of the medicine man, Kesee Pay, Sandy had many conversations with Papeet. She not only attended to his wounds and personal comfort but told him many things about their local customs and taught him local idioms of the language spoken by her people and she pointed out to him differences between it and the dialects he had learned from the Indians of the Bay.

Kesee Pay encouraged this because he saw that it would keep Sandy's mind from brooding too much about his enforced sojourn away from his white friends, and because he hoped that increasing Sandy's proficiency in their language would be beneficial to all of them.

Each time that Sandy spoke with Papeet the more he had a feeling that he had known her before—a feeling that they were not really strangers but were old friends who had been parted for a long time. He realized that he could not have known her before but the feeling persisted along with an increasing sense of mystery and wonderment why he should feel that way.

One sunny afternoon soon after the winter camp had been reestablished, the medicine man, Kesee Pay, said to Sandy, "Now that you are well enough to talk without undue tiring, I think it is time I asked you some serious questions about that metal plate that was hanging from your neck the day we were attacked by the Dakotas on the Red River of the South."

"Very well," said Sandy, "I am ready to tell you all I know about it, and I am curious to know why you are so interested in such a thing."

"I will gladly tell you all I know," said the medicine man, "but first I would ask you a question. Do you know the significance of the markings on the metal plate?"

"No," replied Sandy. "I do not know whether these markings have or have not any special meaning. They are obviously man-made but by whom or for what purpose I can not even guess. I know only that the man who gave it to me believed the plate to be some kind of a magical charm that had belonged to his ancestors when they came to this world 'from the Evening Star.' He believed that it would protect the bearer from death by violence, but not from death by natural causes, because he was dying from some physical illness when he gave it to me. He believed that he had been told in a vision to give it to me and that I was to protect it, because through me the plate would be 'returned to its other half.' He could not, or would not, give me any details about the meaning of the markings on the plate except that they had something to do with the ancient language; but just what that might be did not seem to be clear to him."

"But how did it happen that he picked you instead of someone else to whom the plate should be given?" asked the medicine man.

"It is a rather complicated story," replied the big white man, "but if you are prepared to listen to a long story I will be glad to tell you all I know on the subject."

"I would truly like to hear it, no matter how long or involved it may be," answered the medicine man earnestly, "but if you are willing, I would like my daughter also to listen to your story—for reasons I shall explain later."

To this Sandy readily agreed. He said that in his baggage, among his many notebooks, should be found a book in which he had written, in English, a story of his experiences with the man who had given him the piece of metal disk. If that could be found he would read it to them in the Indian language.

5
SKOTTY'S STORY

The book was found, in good condition, and on the following morning Sandy began reading and slowly translating the text in the hope that Papeet and her father would understand what he had written several years earlier.

The English text in his notebook was as follows:

For several summers I had been sailing on ships between Britain and North America. In the autumn of the year 1716 the ship I was on was captured by pirates when we were not far from the port of Boston, Massachusetts. Because of my size and strength the pirate Captain Bellamy[5] spared me from death and forced me to work at helping to repair and refit his ship during the following winter. Among others with me was a fellow captive who had been seized when the pirates went ashore to raid a small village, to steal corn for food on the ship. This man had the appearance of an Indian but he spoke English fluently; and because he appeared to be husky and strong, the pirate captain had him taken back to the ship, where he had been held for only a short time before I was captured. We spent the winter in a secluded and sheltered cove unknown to other white men.

Many times I was befriended by this man and he and I were drawn together by some unknown attraction. We spent much time together talking but we were very carefully guarded by our captors to prevent our attempting to escape. He was known as Skotty and claimed to be forty-three years of age and was a medicine man of some renown among his native people, but he told me that, although considered by the pirates to be a full-blooded Indian, he was part white and his father's father was a white man.

In the early spring our ship was ready to go out on the open sea and Skotty and I were forced to serve in her as ordinary seamen.

We were at sea only a few days when we were overtaken by a great gale and snow storm. The ship ran aground and Skotty and I were washed overboard, but in some way I received a severe blow on the head and a broken bone in my left arm and would have drowned if Skotty had not supported me on a piece of floating wreckage and kept me from freezing to death after we were blown onto the shore. Skotty and I, after many difficulties, succeeded in finding our way back to his home village, where he introduced me to his friends as the man who had saved *his* life while we were held as slaves of the pirates.

Of course, I did not know much of the Indian language, but Skotty had a very good command of the English language and I soon learned many Indian expressions; and with Skotty acting as interpreter I got along very well with his friends.

When he and I were washed ashore and I had regained my senses, I noticed that he was most concerned about whether he had lost something hidden in his breechcloth and attached to a thong wrapped around his waist. When he found that it was secure he promised to tell me later what it was. He did so, and what he told me was so interesting that I am going to ask him to repeat it and I shall write it down exactly as he tells it to me, in his own words.

"I then asked Skotty to speak slowly because I would try to write the words exactly as he would say them, and this is what I wrote, in the words of Skotty."

"My Indian name is ESKOO-TAYOO but I have long been called 'Skotty' by white men, for two reasons; firstly, because it is a short form of my Indian name, and, secondly, because my real surname in English would be Skott or Scott, since my paternal grandfather was a white man named Ben Skott.

"My grandmother, the wife of Ben Skott, was an Indian girl. Some of her children were more white than Indian, and some were more Indian than white; and the same thing could be said about some of her children's children. My father showed so little of the Indian in his features and characteristics that he usually passed as a white man, as did one of my brothers, but I was a throwback to my grandmother's ancestry. Because of that, I was a great favorite of hers. She taught me the Indian language and much Indian lore, particularly all she knew about the work of Indian medicine men. She was the daughter of a famous medicine man who lived in Connecticut until he was killed in the so-called 'Pequot War' in the year 1637. Her name was Paykee, but by the white people she was generally called Peggy which was the short name for Margaret.

"She was twelve years of age when her father was killed and she and her ten-year-old sister Maylee were taken as prisoners by the Massachusetts Indians who were fighting on the side of the colonists.

"In July, 1637, the two sisters were taken to the vicinity of Boston. After being held a short time by the Indians who had captured them, both girls were sold to white settlers as indentured servants for seven years. This was in accordance with the white man's law and custom that allowed human beings, regardless of color, to be bought and sold as so-called 'indentured servants.'

"That meant that the 'indentured servant' was actually a slave of his or her owner for the stated number of years, unless released by court order, and could be sold to other owners for the unexpired term of the original 'indenture' or service. More precisely, a 'slave' was a human being who was owned outright, with no time limitation of service. Some of the fanatically religious white settlers were against the idea of owning 'slaves' but they were not at all averse to buying, selling, or owning 'indentured servants,' although for the time of their service the latter were little better than slaves.

"The only real slaves that I ever saw were black people. My Indian people always believed that there was a much greater difference between the white people and the black people than there was difference between the white people and the Indians.

"In the early days some white people had tried to make slaves of Indians but they soon gave up that idea. Indians might be forced to submit for a short time but they were never docile servants and as quickly as possible escaped to their friends in the forests.

"The white people did not look upon the system of 'indentured servants' as being something tht brought lifetime disgrace upon the person involved. Some of the best men and women of the white people in our country had been indentured servants. It was often an agreed upon long-term contract to serve for a stated number of years in repayment for something that the 'servant' could not otherwise pay for. Some white people had of their own free will signed bonds to become indentured servants in order to pay for their passage to this country and for being provided with the means of livelihood while learning how to live in what they called 'the New World.' Others were persons who were poor or in debt, in the Old World, or were too young to look after themselves, and their parents or guardians were glad to get rid of them by shipping them to the New World as indentured servants.

"After the stated number of years of service the person was set free of any further service to his or her owner. Also, when good reasons could be shown, the white man's courts could declare a servant to be set at liberty and so become a free person before the end of the time specified in the bond. This sometimes happened when the 'owner' of a female servant wished her to be set free of her bond so that he, or a friend, could marry her—provided, of course, that the woman wished to be set free for that purpose.

"White people did not marry life-long slaves but many did marry persons who had been indentured servants whose time of service had expired or had been ended by order of the white man's courts.

"Before King Phillip's war brought such strife between whites and Indians, the strenuous efforts of the Reverend John Eliot, and others like him, to have the 'praying Indians'—converted or christianized Indians—recognized as socially equal to the white, resulted in many marriages between the white settlers and the christianized Indians. Later, the children of these unions suffered. Those who were too strongly of Indian appearance were sometimes sent into the forest to live with their Indian relatives while some who were only a little of the appearance of Indians were able to be accepted as whites who had inherited 'Black Irish' or 'Black Highlander' coloring. So many of the families were involved that few dared to gossip about others.

"My grandmother, Paykee, was sold to a white family named Skott. The family included a son 'Ben,' about ten years older than Paykee, and a daughter 'Susie,' about two years younger than Paykee.

"In the same village there was a family named Morriss who purchased Paykee's sister Maylee. They had only one child, a little girl called 'Nannie' who was about the same age as Maylee.

"The two Indian girls were not badly treated by their owners and, although they had to help with the housework and the outdoor work, they were treated as members of the family and received the same food, clothing, religious instruction and schooling as did the other children. They were strictly under the control of their masters and mistresses, and the sternly religious owners believed that they were doing the right and proper thing in saving the souls of the girls from heathenism and turning them into good Christians.

"My grandmother had received some training from her father, who had been a famous medicine man of the Pequots. Shortly before he had been killed, he hd given to her a small metal plate which he told her to wear hidden where no man could see it, and she was to keep it close to her at all times and to treat it as a most sacred relic of the ancient times of our ancestors. In the small village, Paykee and Maylee were allowed to visit back and forth. After a year, Paykee and Susie were like sisters, and so were Maylee and Nannie.

"One night in the year 1640, Nannie Morriss was allowed to spend the night with Susie Skott, and Paykee was allowed to spend the night with her sister Maylee in the Morriss home. The sisters were asleep in the loft of the Morriss house when they were gently wakened by a strange but beautiful woman, with long wavy red hair, whose garments were of strange design and gave off a soft light which lit up the tiny room where the girls had been sleeping.

"The woman warned them, softly, not to make any noise, and she began to talk to them in a low voice and in the Indian language.

"My grandmother remembered every word the strange woman said, and often repeated them to me, and I now repeat them to you. Looking at Paykee she said:

'Do not be afraid of me. I am your friend. I come to help you. I am not a mortal woman. I am your "Dream Spirit," your Guardian Spirit or what the white people would call your "Guardian Angel." We Guardian Angels are servants of the Great Spirit of Nature. Other servants are the "Experimenting Angels" who help the Great Spirit to create new things, great and small, but we Guardian Angels have many duties to perform in helping human beings to live. One of my duties is to be your guardian spirit and, from time to time, I may visit you to give you advice. Please listen attentively.'

"The girls listened while the Dream Spirit-woman told them many things.

"One thing in particular my grandmother was fond of repeating to me. I will repeat it to you just as the strange woman spoke the words:

'You two girls are what the white people near you call Indians or Redskins and they imagine that they are much superior to you in everything, and that you are savages while they are civilized.

'I am here to tell you that what the white people think about you and your people is very much in error.

'Both your people and the white people are descended from some of the same kind of people of ages ago. Your people's ancestors lived for long ages in one kind of country and theirs lived in lands having different conditions. Intermarriage with other races brought changes and differences resulting in the differences we now see between your people and the white people.

'The people of the oldest race of your ancestors were much more like what some of the white people are now than you are now like the white people. Those people of the oldest race of your ancestors were most renowned for their intelligence, knowledge and skills. It was they who taught the other peoples of the earth, and, by many of the latter, they were looked upon as gods.

'Those highly skilled and intelligent people had wavy red hair, like mine, while the lesser races had straight back or colorless hair such as you have or as so many of the white people have in various combinations of shades. All this that we see now is because you, like the present white people, now have the blood and instincts of some of the lesser races as well as that of the old red-haired race.

'I want you two girls to realize that you are descendants of a very ancient race of people who had a state of civilization far, far higher than anything known on this whole earth today. Even the most lowly servants of your ancestors of the red-haired race were more intelligent, better informed about natural things and the universe, and, in ways far beyond your intelligence to understand, were more civilized and better educated and better behaved than any group or nation of so-called white men in this world of today. Do not ever forget this. Do not ever be ashamed that you are what your present white owners and their neighbors call "Indian savages." Black-haired "Indians" you may be now, but you are also descendants of the great wavy red-haired race that was powerful and great long before the first black-haired, white-skinned people were transplanted on this planet as a minor experiment of scientists of a minor world in the sky.

'Always have pride in your racial ancestry. Do not try to pretend

29

that you are something different from what you are. You are what you are because you were born that way and you should always be proud that you are what you are. No white person can do anything that you can not do if you try hard enough. Of course, you would first have to learn all the things that the white people have learned in the past few hundred years while your people have been busy learning other things in lands not overrun by the self-styled "civilized" white people. Always remember that brain for brain you are in no way inferior to the white people.

'I tell you this because, as far as you two girls are concerned, the time has come when you must try to become, in outward appearance, like the white people, and you must adopt the ways of the white people and marry white men.

'Perhaps when the long-separated blood strains come together there may be, in time, a return to the civilized status of long, long ago. Any time you see people with hair of the color and texture of mine you will know that you are seeing a partial throwback to your people and my people of the ancient times. The blood strain of that race has been diluted and contaminated by mixture with blood strains of other races and by stagnation within groups of people living long in one place.

'It will take many years for the return to anything like the ancient state of civilization, but each of you is destined to do a part in the slow but steady process.

'I am here, tonight, to tell you something of what is in store for you and your descendants if you will follow my advice—for I can only influence, I can not control, your actions.

'Both of you must do all you can to learn from the white people, to become as competent as any white woman in all things known to the white women of today—little as that may be in comparison with the accomplishments of women of your face fifty thousand years ago.

'Each of you is to marry a white man, and some, but not all, of your children and your grandchildren will be considered as members of the white race. Paykee will do much to help the sick and afflicted, and may, in the end receive strange thanks for it. Maylee will be the mother of seven daughters, and the seventh daughter will be the mother of one of the most wise and most famous men in this part of the world. His name and fame will be known in every household in this country, and to wise men all over the world, and will remain well-known for many generations to come. Few, if any, men except himself will long remember his part-Indian ancestry or know that much of his remarkable intelligence came in the form of inherited memories from his long dead ancestors of our ancient race.

'To excel, the white man, the Indian, or the member of any other race, must first acquire all the knowledge and acquired abilities of the white man and then must add his own inherited abilities, and must improve and expand them all. This will be a slow process, as I have said, but time is of little importance in the schemes of nature. Time is one thing of which the Great Spirit has a bountiful supply.

'You two girls have been destined to do your important parts in furthering the work of the Great Spirit. You must adopt and practice the teachings of the white praying-men or clergymen—but not necessarily the actions of many white people who follow only parts of the things they hear from such clergymen. You must do what you can to help your Indian kinsmen to understand that the real God of the white man is the same Great Spirit we know, but as seen through different kinds of colored glass. In all this, you must cooperate with, and not antagonize, the people with whom you deal— white or Indian.

'Paykee, one of your sons will join the congregation of a white clergyman who is now in this country and who will be given credit for the translation of the white man's "Holy Scriptures" into the language of the Indians, although the dialect he will use will be a very corrupted form of the ancient language. In his work on the Indian tongue, this clergyman will be assisted by your son.

'A great-grandson of yours will marry a great-grand-daughter of Maylee, and a descendant of that union will be an important instrument in bringing together the two long-separated half sections of the Golden Talisman. I am speaking now of the talisman of solid gold, for the talisman which is now in your possession, Paykee, is but a base-metal duplicate of one of two sections of the real Golden Talisman; but your talisman will play a very important part in bringing together the two long-separated sections. Some day in the future a red-haired man and a red-haired woman, both speaking

31

our language, will bring together the two halves of the Golden Talisman, and they shall be joined together. You must guard your talisman very carefully until I return to tell you what to do with it. You must tell no white person about my visit or about the things I have told you.

'Paykee, you must do everything you can to help your sister to become a good wife and mother, as you yourself must be.

'Now, girls, I must leave you. No one has heard me talking to you because no sounds have been made. My spirit voice has talked to your spirits, and when you wake in the morning my visit with you will seem to have been only a vivid dream. But please remember every word you have heard from me, for this has been no ordinary dream. Now, close your eyes and go to sleep. May the Great Spirit help me to watch over you both and may He keep you on the right paths of life until we meet again.'

"When the girls awoke in the morning each told the other about the strange dream she had had. Then they realized that just as the Dream Spirit had said, this had been *'no ordinary dream.'*

"This happened in the year 1640, and two years later the Skott family applied to the Court of Assistants in Boston to have Paykee declared at liberty to be married to their son, Ben. The court did so and Paykee and Ben were married.

"In the meantime, a young man had arrived from across the ocean, five years earlier, and was very determined to learn the language of the Indians, in order to help christianize the Indians and to help him in his work with Indians as a land surveyor and map maker. He was a frequent visitor at the Morriss home. He found Maylee to be very helpful because of her knowledge of the Indian tongue. He became very fond of her, and when he learned that Paykee and Ben were to be married, he persuaded the Morriss family to sell to him the girl Maylee, or Mary, as she was now called by the white people, so that he could take her to the home of his employer, on the island known as 'The Vineyard,' until she would be old enough to be his wife. This man was named Peter Voltsher and he worked for a man named Thomas Mayhew. Peter paid twenty pounds for Mary, and, immediately after the marriage of my grandmother, he took Mary to The Vineyard, and for two years she lived in the Mayhew household there. Peter and Mary were married, and they had two sons and seven daughters.

"I was born in the year 1673. My father was always like a white man, and being a good member of the Reverend John Eliot's congregation at Roxbury was considered to be as good as any of the other members of that congregation; but I was different. I had more Indian features than my father and all my inclinations and instaincts were Indian rather than white. I was very fond of my grandmother and she was fond of me. She said I resembled her father. She taught me all the Indian lore she remembered and I always used the Indian language when talking with her.

"I was shown the sacred talisman she guarded so carefully. She repeatedly told me what the woman in the vision, the female Dream Spirit, had said to her and her sister. My grandmother used many Indian remedies to help cure illnesses in the villages and both Indian and white people respected her highly as a doctor. She had helpfully treated many a white child, and that child's children, because she lived for fifty years after her marriage. My grandfather died many years before she did.

"In the spring and summer of the year 1692, there was a terrible affliction of the minds of many of the people in the vicinity of Boston who called themselves good Christians. It was as if the devil of the white man's religion had set their minds on fire and destroyed all their sense of Christian behaviour. They became crazed like animals with a lust to kill or to see helpless persons tortured physically and mentally. They lost all sense of fair play, gratitude or kindness. People were accused of being witches, on fantastic charges, by silly children and ignorant adults. The accused were often officially murdered because they could *not* prove they were *not* witches any more than their judges *could* prove that they were.

"On the first day of September, 1692, my grandmother sent for me. She told me that during the night she had been visited by the vision of the Dream Spirit woman and had been told to give me the sacred talisman which she had guarded so long. The Dream Spirit thanked my grandmother for all she had done to follow the instructions she had been given so many years before, but the Dream Spirit very sadly told her that in three weeks her life would be taken by the witch hunt-crazed white people who would be acting under what they mistakenly believed to be the orders of their Great Spirit. She was to turn over the sacred talisman to me and she was to tell me to guard it carefully until I would be told what to do with it.

"Soon after that I learned that one of the members of a family of four children accused my grandmother of being a witch and said that she had bewitched one of their children and the child had died. These people seemed to forget that my grandmother had nursed all four children through a severe illness and by her knowledge and tender care had saved the lives of three children, but the youngest, a sickly child since birth, she had been unable to save.

"At the time, the parents had been full of praise for the way my grandmother had saved the lives of the three older children and they had realized that it was through no fault of my grandmother that the youngest and frailest child had died. But, when the witch hunt craze overcame the people, those parents were among the most insistent that it was because of my grandmother that their 'bewitched' child had died. They forgot all about the three other children whose lives my grandmother had saved. They claimed that one of the children had seen a 'devil's badge' of metal worn by my grandmother and that it had on it 'markings made in the devil's own handwriting.'

"My grandmother was arrested and was stripped naked and searched but the 'devil's badge' could not be found. They searched her house for it and when they could not find it, they set fire to her house, hoping to destroy the 'devil's badge.'

"In spite of her age, the poor old woman was tortured to try to make her tell what she had done with the 'unholy charm.' She would tell them nothing.

"On the twenty-second day of September, 1692, where a large oak tree stood on a hill within sight of a Christian church, a crowd of self-styled 'pure Christians' watched excitedly and happily, like crazed animals, while my poor widowed grandmother and six other women were put to death because they were believed to be witches.

"From that day forth I pondered more and more about the old Indian beliefs of the one Great Spirit, for we had no *Evil Spirit* in our beliefs until the white men told us about him and insisted that we must accept him as the great rival of our own *Good Spirit*.

"When I first met you, something seemed to attract me to you, as if you were a kinsman or an old friend of boyhood days that I could barely remember. Something about your wavy red hair seemed to fascinate me, and it reminded me constantly of the stories my

34

grandmother had told me about the wavy red hair of the woman Dream Spirit who had twice visited her."

This is the end of what Sandy read from his book.*

---

*This is an only slightly fictionalized story about two ancestresses of the writer of this story. "Peggy" was one of the "Salem Witches" executed near Boston, Massachusetts, on the 22nd day of September, 1692 A.D. In the official records of the State of Massachusetts, "Records of the Court of Assistants, 28 of the 5th month, 1642, page 125" her name is shown as Margaret; "Margaret Stephenson is judged at liberty to be married to Benjamin Scott." At her trial and execution she was known as "Margaret Scott of Rowley."[6]

The other ancestress, whose great-grand-daughter married a great-grandson of Margaret Stephenson Scott, was "Mary," the maternal grandmother of Dr. Benjamin Franklin. Mary was the wife of Peter Folger. About her origin and surname there is mystery and conflicting evidence, but various books by or about Dr. Benjamin Franklin show that his grandfather bought Mary for twenty pounds and later married her. Peter Folger was an interpreter of the Indian language and teacher of Indians on Martha's Vineyard and Nantucket with the Mayhews. (See: Van Doren, *Benjamin Franklin* (The Viking Press, 1938), p. 7.)

6
SANDY LEARNS ABOUT THE TALISMAN

The solemn-faced medicine man had listened attentively to the white man's story, and so had his daughter.

"I am very interested," he said, "in several things you have mentioned. I can understand about the spirit or angel helpers of the Great Spirit because they are part of our people's belief in the ways of the Great Spirit of Nature, as I shall be happy to try to explain to you at another time. But first I would like to hear how the section of the sacred talisman came into your possession."

Sandy had read all he had written but continued his story.

"In the following year, 1718, I was navigator and mate of a ship engaged to carry a large number of men, women and children from the port of Londonderry in Northern Ireland to the port of Boston in Massachusetts, North America. These people, or their parents, and in some cases their grandparents, had left their homes in Scotland and had settled in the part of Ireland just across the water from Scotland. They were people to whom religion was a very, very serious matter. They had their own ideas about religion, which differed greatly from the older religion known as the Roman Catholic faith. Their ideas also differed from the ideas of religion held by the English people.

"The English had been at war with the Roman Catholic people of Ireland and had captured or taken possession of a vast block of land in the northern part of that great island. The English had the idea that if they should transplant some of those troublesome Scottish people on the land taken from the Irish, the Scots and the Irish would be too busy fighting each other for either side to continue being very troublesome to the English.

"Things did not work out quite as the English had hoped, and not only did the Scots and their Irish neighbours get along reasonably well, but the Scots, now called the "Scotch-Irish" or the "Ulster-

Scots," became very industrious, particularly in the industry of growing and processing flax and producing linen cloth. In a few years they became serious competitors with English cloth makers, and the latter prevailed on the English government to pass oppressive, restrictive laws that made life very difficult for the Ulster-Scots, many of whom decided to emigrate to America where they could practice their own religion and work under less oppressive laws. Our ship carried many of them to New England in that summer of 1718.

"One day in August, 1718, while our ship was in the port of Boston, Massachusetts, an Indian came to me and told me that my old friend Skotty was very ill in a village a few miles away, but was very anxious that I should talk with him. I arranged with my Captain to have time to go to visit my Indian friend. I reached his home with the help of the man he had sent to find me. I found Skotty very ill but still able to talk. He told me that a few nights ago he had seen the vision of the same Dream Spirit woman who had visited his grandmother. She told him that he must send for me and that he must turn over to me the metal talisman that he had received from his grandmother.

"The Dream Spirit had told Skotty that 'A red-haired man and a red-haired woman would some day bring together the two long-separated half-sections of the Golden Talisman (of which the metal plate in Skotty's possession was only a base-metal copy of one section of the original gold plate) and that they would be joined together.'

"I tried to learn from him what had happened to the original plate. He either did not know or could not tell me, but kept insisting that I promise to keep and protect the talisman. I promised to do so. He tried to tell me something more but died before I could make understandable anything of what he was trying to say. That is my story of what I know about this mysterious piece of metal," concluded the big white man.

The Indian medicine man, who had listened intently to every word, then asked, "Have you ever seen or heard of the other half of what must have been the original gold plate?"

"No," answered Sandy. "I have neither seen nor heard a word about it, but when I first saw your daughter, as I recovered consciousness in your lodge, it flashed into my mind—'Here is the red-haired girl the Dream Spirit said would have the other half of the Golden Talisman.' But I quickly realized that this could not be so because I did not have 'the other half of the gold plate'—I had only a base-metal copy of it. So I said nothing to her about it."

"Very, very strange," said the medicine man in a low voice, speaking to himself; then, addressing the white man, he said, "Did I understand you correctly to say that your friend Skotty said that 'a red-haired woman and a red-haired man would bring together the two halves of the Golden Talisman *and they would be joined together*'?"

"Yes," said Sandy, "that is exactly what he told me."

"When you were talking with Skotty were you using the English language, or the Indian tongue?" asked the medicine man.

"We were using English," answered Sandy. "At that time I was unable to speak the Indian tongue fluently."

"Now that you are speaking in the Indian tongue," said his companion, "you use the word for 'they,' which means that the materials represented by that word were inanimate objects, and I assume you believed the English word 'they' used by Skotty meant 'they— two metal objects'—in other words, that 'they' (the two pieces of metal) would be joined together. But there is another possible meaning of what Skotty said.

"As you now know from your knowledge of the Indian language, if Skotty had been speaking in the Indian tongue the word used for 'they' would have clearly indicated whether it referred to inanimate objects, such as the metal plates, or to animate objects, such as the man and the woman, or to a mixed group including both the metal pieces and the persons. Perhaps the English language, like some of the Indian dialects I have heard, is not so precise in such matters as is our language. Perhaps Skotty meant one thing and you understood something else. What I am wondering about is, did the Dream Spirit mean that the red-haired man and the red-haired woman, each possessing a section of the metal plate, would be 'joined together'?"

"I never thought about that," said Sandy in a tone of astonishment. "I thought only about the two pieces of metal, not about the persons, but it could well be that the Dream Spirit made that matter clear to Skotty and while talking to me in English he was thinking about the two persons and not about the two metal sections.

38

The English language is not nearly so precise in such matters as is your Indian language—Nayhewaywaywin—'the way of speaking precisely.' "

"Now, to go back to your story," said the medicine man. "You did not mention anything about the talisman to my daughter. You know she must have seen that which you were carrying when struck by the Dakota arrow. It may surprise you to know that she would have been very much interested if you had asked her about the other half of the Golden Talisman—because she has seen it and knows where it is."

"She does!" exclaimed Sandy in surprise. "How does she know where it is?"

"Because I have it," said the medicine man with a smile.

"Do you mean that you have the original of the half that I have, or the other half?"

"I mean that I have the part of the original Golden Talisman that joins the part for which you have a copy. I know nothing of the whereabouts of the part for which you have the copy. The part I have is gold, not base-metal like yours, but the zigzag edges of the gold section and the edges of your section fit together exactly, so there can be no mistake."

"Then there is one half of the Golden Talisman that is still missing?" asked the white man.

"Yes," said the Indian. "The so-called 'Eastern Half' of it is still missing, but with your copy of it the whole design becomes understandable and the words represented by the markings can be understood."

Kesee Pay then showed Sandy the two sections of the talisman fitted together, but saying, as he did so, "There is a design on each side but apparently they are not related to each other. This side which is now before us I can understand, but I have to admit that I know nothing about the meaning of the design on the other side."

Sandy could see many strange lines, curves and angles but they meant nothing to him. Kesee Pay, however, assured him that these contained the great secret of the sound symbols that could be used for writing (or printing) the Indian language.

"Do you mean to tell me," said the surprised Sandy, "that you can read the markings and understand them?"

"Yes, of course," said the Indian with pride in his voice. "The

Golden Talisman carries the key to the written language of my ancestors and the motto or message engraved around it is in our ancient tongue."

"What does it mean?" inquired the white man eagerly.

"It means," said the medicine man solemnly an reverently, " 'The Great Spirit helps those who help themselves and one another.' It also could be said to mean, 'The Great Spirit helps those who help Him to help them.' "

"Then," said the white man, with awe in his voice, "the original golden disk must have been the key to the written language of prehistoric America."

East Half

West Half

The Golden Talisman
from Outer Space—
the Golden Key to
Prehistoric Knowledge

7
THE DREAM AND PEYO-WAH-MIT

On the following day Kesee Pay said to Sandy, "You have told me so much about yourself that I think it is only right that I should tell you about myself. I was born fifty winters ago. My father was known by the name Mistamiskoo, or 'Big Beaver.' His father was known as Peyo-wah-mit, or 'He Who Dreams.' Peyo-wah-mit had inherited our half of the Golden Talisman from his grandfather, Moosoom. We belonged to a long line of medicine men and tradition tellers of our nation, 'The Precisely Speaking People.'

"My grandfather, Peyo-wah-mit, was the most renowned of our line because he was the first to revive the use of our written language which had become forgotten because of disuse.

"A messenger from the unseen world of the Great Spirit taught my grandfather how to write, and he taught his son, my father, who taught me . . . although my grandfather also taught me the use of the syllabic system of writing.

"My grandfather, who lived until I had passed twenty-five winters, also taught me many things and insisted that I practice the art of writing and that I, in my turn, should teach all I might know to my son. Unfortunately, I have no son, but, from her childhood, I have taught my daughter in all my skills and knowledge. That is how it happens that she knows our system of writing our language; actually she has much greater facility in its use than I have.

"It was my grandfather who urged me to travel and to visit other nations and to learn medicine skills and languages from many different people.

"After my grandfather had been taught to use the long-forgotten system of writing our language, he had been given information which he had written in books of blank paper he had obtained from white men from the east. He had been instructed to place these books in an airtight container and to hide them in a certain specified place. He had done this before I was born, but he gave me detailed instructions about the location of the books, for me to pass on to my heir. The books were not to be opened until the missing half of the Golden Talisman 'came to join the half' which was then in his possession.

"I am now in a quandary, because I do not know whether I should open the container and read the books, or whether I should let them remain as they are. The missing half of the talisman has come to join my grandfather's half but it is not the real golden half, although it must be an exact copy made of some other metal. My problem is to decide whether I should or should not remove the books from their hiding place and make known their contents to you. I do not wish to displease the Great Spirit by having the contents of the book revealed too soon. On the other hand, however, perhaps it is fitting and proper that I do reveal the contents to you. It is because of this problem that I have been so careful in collecting so much information from you by means of your normal waking memories before I make my decision. But there is one other thing I should do; I should have my daughter read to you from one of the books written by my grandfather Peyo-wah-mit, and together we will try to explain some of the things to you.

"First of all, I should tell you about something you may already know, but in case you do not, I shall begin by saying that it has long been a custom of our people for boys to go through certain ordeals or trials before they can be considered to be men. One such ordeal calls for the boy, or young man as he then considers himself, to go alone to a desolate place and to fast and to pray to the Great Spirit until he sees a vision in which a spirit from the dream world, a dream spirit, will visit him and will give him advice on how to act as a man. This dream spirit will be his spiritual guardian for the remainder of his life although perhaps never seen again or perhaps seen only occasionally; but the boy, now become a man, will always feel the close presence of his dream spirit and will try to do nothing to offend the wishes of his spiritual guardian.

"My grandfather Peyo-wah-mit, in due course, went to a place we call the 'Sacred Hill,' a cave near the top of a desolate rocky hill in the forest several days travel to the east of where we are now. He performed the necessary ritual and was visited by a dream spirit but, to his great surprise, his guardian spirit was not a man as he had expected to see but was a woman—a woman with long wavy red hair such as you described in your story about the dream spirit that visited Skotty's grandmother Paykee. It is that part of your story which amazed me so much and caused me to do much meditation on the things you have told me and on the things told to me by my grandfather and things contained in his writings which are now in my possession.

"He wrote several books which I have never seen but about which he has told me much. The books which my daughter will now read to you tell what happened to him after he had visited the Sacred Hill and conversed with the Dream Spirit—Powakun—several times.

"He had been taught how to write our language and had been given certain duties to perform, as instructed by the Dream Spirit. He had been told to go home and to practice the use of the writing symbols and to write certain things which he should show to the Dream Spirit on his next visit to the Sacred Hill.

"Among other things, the dream spirit had instructed my grandfather to copy the full design as we have seen it on the sacred talisman. He was told to make a copy of it on a plate of copper such as was used by the white fur traders for making riveted copper kettles for trade with other people. On one side of the plate were shown more details of the individual symbols.

"Now, Papeet will read to you, but if there is any point on which you desire some explanation, please do not hesitate to interrupt her, and we will discuss the point."

Papeet was holding what appeared to Sandy to be a trader's account book of ordinary paper and binding of the time, but the pages seemed to be covered with the strange symbols of triangles, hooks and angles he had so often seen on the sacred talisman. He was amazed that Papeet could read from the book as easily as he could read from a book printed in English.

She began to read, slowly, the words written by Peyo-wah-mit, grandson of Moosoom, as follows:

"I must write about things that happened and about things that were told to me to be recorded and passed on for the information and benefit of my people.

"The things to be recorded are the important things. I, myself, am not important; therefore, I shall begin by writing about them not as if seen through my own eyes or as heard through my own ears but as if seen and heard by some person other than myself.

And so I begin:

The First Book of Peyo-Wah-Mit

In front of a neat and tidy birchbark wigwam, in the forested area between that great body of drinkable water known in the Nay-he-ya-way-oo language as Kitshe Kumee—The Great Body of Water—and the northward-flowing river to the westward, known as Mikoo Seepee—The Red River—two men of the Nay-he-ya-way-oo nation were talking.

The younger man would more accurately be described as a boy, for he had not yet reached the official tribal status of a "man" among his people, although he was tall, strong, and well built and apparently full grown and in good health. His face showed him to be intelligent and of an inquiring and thoughtful nature.

The older man, also, was tall, strong, and intelligent looking. He wore the garb of a tribal medicine man. Prominent among the decorations he wore was a small pouch or bag of beaded leather hanging at his breast from a leather thong around his neck.

The solemn and thoughtful eyes of the boy were focused on the beaded leather bag as he spoke to the elderly man.

"Please tell me, my grandfather," said he, "is it true that the piece of yellow metal with the strange markings, that hangs from your neck, was brought to our land by one of our ancestors of the red-haired race, before the great catastrophe that destroyed so many of our people?"

"Yes, Peyo-wah-mit, my grandson," replied the medicine man, "I believe that to be true but I have only traditions on which to base my belief. Our tribal traditions tell us that, many many winters ago, a man and a woman came, as leaders of a party of men and women of an ancient red-haired race, seeking descendants of long lost colonists from their homeland. Something went wrong with the strange, large canoe that brought them, and they could not begin their return journey until certain rare materials were found and collected and used in making repairs. From the local people, the strangers learned of far places where it might be possible to obtain the materials they so badly needed.

"An expedition, or party, of our people, led by the red-haired woman, traveled to a country far to the northwest, and another party of our people, led by the red-haired man, began a long journey to the east. While the two expeditions were far away, there was a terrible catastrophe in our old homeland and it was many generations before the descendants of our ancestors who had been led by the red-haired woman found their way back to the desolate land.

"Before the two expeditions had started away, a gold talisman carried by the man had been cut into two equal parts by a peculiar zig-zag cut. One half was given to the woman, and the man retained the other half."

"Can you tell me, my grandfather, the meaning of the markings on your half of the talisman?" inquired the boy.

"Again we have only traditions to guide us," answered his grandfather, "but the markings are believed to contain the key to the secrets of the art of writing."

"By 'art of writing,'" said the boy earnestly, "do you mean the strange ability which travelers and story tellers from the east tell us is possessed by the white-skinned strangers who came to our land from the other side of the great salt-water lake—the ability for a man to make marks that other men can talk to and will say the same words that any other man would say while talking to those marks?"

"Something like that," smiled the grandfather. "I have been told that a white man can hold in his hand a thing he calls a 'book.' He talks to the book and says the words that the marks in the book tell him to say. Another white man can look at the same book and when he talks to it he will say the same words that the first man said, even if many moons have passed since the marks were made."

"If I knew how to make the proper marks," said the boy seriously, "I could write our stories and traditions so they would not be forgotten or changed from time to time."

"You are a wise young man, in spite of your having only sixteen winters," admitted the older man. "It should indeed be possible for you to write records of many things, if only you knew how to write. But no living person knows how to write our language. Travelers from the east and from the northeast tell us that on the shores of the great salt lake some white men have been living for over fifty winters and some of them know how to write their own language, but our people have not learned the secret of writing in our own language."

"If the secret of writing our language is hidden in the markings of

45

the talisman you wear, why can not some of our wise men find out that secret?" asked the boy eagerly.

"Because," replied his grandfather, "only half of the secret is here. Half of the markings must be on the missing half of the original talisman, and unless the two halves are exactly fitted together again the whole of the markings can not be known."

"I wish I could learn to write in my own language," said the boy with a solemn face. Then his face lit up as he spoke to his grandfather, saying, "There is another thing I would like to ask you, my grandfather."

"Go ahead and ask," was the good-natured reply.

"Yesterday, " said the boy, "I listened to the traveler from the east telling you about the strange customs and actions of those people whose skin is the color of rabbits in winter and who now live in our land far to the east of us near the edge of the great salt lake. One thing I could not understand was the statement that those white-skinned strangers say it is now the year one thousand six hundred and thirty-nine. What does that mean?"

"It means," explained the grandfather, "that the white men count an interval of time from the shortest day of one winter to the shortest day of the next winter and call that whole interval of time 'one year.' The years are numbered consecutively from a starting point established so long ago that the year we are now living in is numbered 1639; meaning that it is now 1639 years since the numbering was commenced. We count our time in moons and in winters. We have a name for each moon but no name or number for each winter."

The boy was still meditating about the things he had been told by his grandfather. He remembered that the latter had mentioned a word which he did not fully understand, so he asked his grandfather another question: "You mentioned something you called a book. Is my understanding correct that a book is something in which a great many markings or much writing can be made, or can you tell me more about it, my grandfather?"

"Yes, my grandson," replied the tall Indian man. "At least you are partly right in your understanding. I have, of course, not seen the thing that the white men look at and talk to but I have been told about it many times. It is what, in our language would be called a *musinahikun*—'a man-made thing, with meaningful markings'—

but in the language of some white men it is called a 'book,' and in the language of some white men, whose praying-men wear black robes, it is called by a name which has in it two sounds not heard in our language.

"The book is not made of birchbark but of sheets of some white material like layers of birchbark, or like layers from a wasp nest but smoother and stronger. These layers are four-sided and on one side they are fastened together so that many layers are contained in one book. On these layers or pages of the book are black markings which are pictures of words of the spoken language of the white men."

"Is it only the white men's languages that can be so shown in pictures?" inquired the boy.

The grandfather replied thoughtfully, "I have been told that these markings can also be used to represent words of some of the white men's languages so old that living men no longer speak them in their ordinary talk, but the praying-men of the white people use some of the old languages when talking to their Great Spirits."

"Do the white men worship more than one Great Spirit?" asked the boy thoughtfully. "Do they not have the same one Great Spirit that we have?"

"No," replied the older man. "I have been told that instead of the one Great Spirit that we worship, some white men have three 'spirits' they always mention as the central things of their religion; all three being spiritual forms of human beings; two of them being very good and one of them being very bad. But the followers of the praying-men of the black robes have four main spirits at the top of their religion. Of these, there are two good men-spirits and one good woman-spirit, and there is one very bad spirit who is like something that is half man and half giant bat with a tail."

"Is it not strange," said the boy, "that although all Indians we know worship the one Great Spirit, the white men are divided and have two different religions?"

"You are right, my wise young grandson," agreed the old man, "it is not only strange, but stranger still is the fact, so I have been told, that two different kinds of white men intend to send their praying-men into the lands of all Indians to tell us that we must cease our worship of our one Great Spirit and that we must worship only their particular group of spirits. Not only that, but the praying-men

47

of each of the white men's religions claim that the other white man's religion is all wrong and we must not listen to the praying-men of the other religion."

"Then the white men, as a whole, do not know which of their two religions is the true religion. Am I right, my grandfather?"

"Yes," replied his grandfather, "it would seem to me that you are right, if I have understood properly what I have been told by men who have known the white men in the east. The praying-men of the white people wish to destroy our one-Great-Spirit religion and force us to accept a many-spirited religion that includes not only good spirits but includes an evil spirit so powerful that even the good 'Great Spirit' can not control him—which is something unknown to us Indians. We know that there are some very minor spirits that play tricks and make fun of people sometimes, but they are nothing we would fear or worship. The praying-men of both religions of the white men are sure that our religion is all wrong, but that is almost the only thing on which they do agree."

"Would it not be more sensible for the white men to settle among themselves upon one religion before trying to destroy ours?" asked the boy. "Instead of coming here to teach us the 'one true religion,' why do they not stay home and teach one another until they all have the same 'one true religion'? How can they expect us to believe that the white man's religion is so much better than ours when they themselves do not know which of theirs is the better?"

"My grandson, for a young man of only sixteen winters, you have asked very sensible questions. Unfortunately, I do not know the proper answers. I think it is about time that you went to the Sacred Hill in hope of finding the answers."

"Well, my grandfather," said the boy, still thinking more about his questions than about the Sacred Hill mentioned by his grandfather, "if all the white men of each religion do follow the teachings of their praying-men, I suppose there are many good men living good lives and doing good deeds in each religious group."

"From what I have been told," admitted the old man sadly, "it would seem that for every one praying-man among the white people who have come to our land, so far, there have been ten men who *do* almost all the things that their praying-men say they *should not do*, and there have been twenty or more other men who pay little or

48

no attention to the words of their praying-men in their day-to-day lives, although many of them do make a great show of doing so on part of one day which comes four times in the time of each moon."

"I can not understand," said the boy, "why the white men wish to come here to teach us when there must be so much greater need to teach their own people."

"The white men," said the old man, shaking his head from side to side, "are very strange people, especially their praying-men. They are like greedy men who can not take the time to see what is under their feet because they are so busy thinking about what they believe to be far better things on the other side of the far away hills."

"Do the books that the white men have tell about their religion?" asked the boy.

"Yes, so I have been told," replied his grandfather.

"If the white men have books on their religion, why do we have no books telling us about our religion?" wondered the boy.

"We have no books now," admitted the old man. "We have no system of writing *pictures of the words we speak*. We can write only *pictures of things we see*. But why are you so interested in all this?"

"I have been thinking, my grandfather," replied the boy soberly, "if the white men can have a system that enables them to keep records of things that happen, or that can enable one person to write something that can be sent many days journey to another person who, by looking at the writing, can talk to it and all men listening to him can hear and understand exactly what the first person said or wrote, would it not be possible for us to make writing in our own language so we could send messages over long distances to others of our race? Would it not be of value to us for keeping records of the tales and traditions of our people; tales that now have to be memorized and passed down from one generation to another?"

"Yes," responded the old man. "There could be many uses for such a system of writing."

The boy continued. "If the white man has a system of writing for his language, how does it happen that we do not? Are we not what almost all people but ourselves call the *K'nistinowuk* or 'The First People'? And, if we were the first people, why do we call ourselves the *Nay-he-ya-way-wuk*, meaning 'The Proper-speaking People'?"

"One question at a time, please," laughed the grandfather. "I shall try to explain what I can, in answer to your questions, but first I would say that you certainly seem to be living up to your name, Peyo-Wah-Mit—'The Dreamer,' or 'The Meditator.' "

"Perhaps, my grandfather, you will tell me why I was given that name," said the boy seriously.

"Years ago," began the grandfather, "I had a big strong son who had a beautiful and most intelligent wife. Most men of our race pray to have a son as his first child, but because my son loved his wife so much he wanted to have a daughter just like her. His wife secretly wanted to have a son just like her husband. Both prayed constantly to the Great Spirit to grant them their desires. As medicine man, I knew the desires of both and I too prayed to the Great Spirit for them and I made all the good medicine I knew. My prayers were answered and my son's wife brought forth twin children, a boy and a girl.

"For three years all went well, but then a mysterious sickness brought death to many of our people, and both my son and his wife were taken from us, and the two little children, the little boy and the little girl, were left to your grandmother, Ookooma, and me to care for; and very happy were we to have them with us.

"Before she lost her parents, the little girl was always happy and laughing. She was at first given the name 'Little Red Loon' but later, as she grew older and her hair became darker, her name was changed to Tukee-Papoo, which as you know means 'Ever Laughing.' The reason she was at first called Little Red Loon was because, in addition to her being like that bird, the loon, that is always laughing, her hair was not jet black like the hair of nearly all Indian girls, but much of it was the color of polished red copper metal, such as is found on the southern shore of the great water known as Kitshe Kumee. You know that a few hairs of my head are still reddish instead of being black like the hair of other men you know. When I was a boy many hairs of my head were red and I was told that that was because, hundreds of winters ago, one of my female ancestors was a woman with long, copper-red hair who came to this world from the Evening Star.

"The little brother was quite different from his twin sister. He seemed to spend most of his time thinking seriously about things or daydreaming—when not asking questions about serious matters. He was always interested in my stories and in stories told by wan-

50

dering 'storytellers' who visited us from time to time. After hearing a story, he always sat and daydreamed about what he had heard. So it was, my grandson, that the boy was called 'The Little Dreamer.' You were that boy, but you are no longer little, so now your grown-up name is Peyo-wah-mit: 'He Who Dreams.'

"You asked me why we do not have a system of writing. My answer to that is that the art of writing or making pictures of the words of our language was lost at the time of the last great catastrophe. But in the ancient days, when our ancestors were among the most wise and most skilled people of the earth, we had a system of writing our language and many books were written. In them was recorded all the things that all the wise men of many generations had learned or had been told by the servants of the Great Spirit. The pages of these books, so tradition tells us, were not made of birch bark or paper that crumbles to dust when old, but they were made of very thin sheets of hammered gold that never changes in texture or color."

"Where are those books now?" asked Peyo-wah-mit.

"That is something no living man knows," replied his grandfather. "We do not know what that catastrophe was or when or where it happened. Some traditions seem to indicate that it was a flood that covered the land with water. Other traditions indicate that it was an explosion after a star fell down from the sky, and this was followed by great fires, and sickness and death among the people who survived the great fires. Other traditions say that our people once lived in great numbers on a very large island, surrounded by salt water that moved away from the shores for a little while and then came back in flood pushed or pulled by the moon; this happening twice in each period of a day and a night.

"The people on that great island, so traditions tell us, had been guided by the Great Spirit to make for themselves many machines and other things made of metal and some kind of stone that was clear like ice but not cold or wet. By means of many kinds of man-made things, these island people had the ability to see and to hear things over great distances. Also, they had huge canoes that moved on the water without being paddled by men. These canoes were so large that men and women could live on them for many days at a time, without returning to land.

"The Great Spirit had allowed these people to have the power to break large masses of rock so they could make roads and dig canals to let fresh water run so that things could be grown for food. But the people had been warned not to use any of these man-made things to do harm to human beings. All gifts of power and skill given by the Great Spirit to the people were to be used only for the benefit of the people, and if the skills and powers were abused and used for anything but the benefit of the people as a whole, they would be withdrawn from these people and given to some other kind of people who might be better able to carry out the desires of the Great Spirit, which were to improve the living conditions of mankind on this earth.

"For many years the people tried to act according to the wishes of the Great Spirit. Many improvements were made and all people worked together, and on all the island there was enough for every person; no one was in dire need, and no one had great wealth in excess of his neighbors. Thus, for many years there was great contentment in the land. People were busy trying to improve things and trying to expand the populated areas, but, in time, mankind split into three kinds of people: the kind of people who tried to continue the kind of life that had made their country great and prosperous by following the wishes of the Great Spirit; the kind of people who were greedy and wanted to have for themselves, as individuals or as groups, more power or more wealth than their neighbors; and the third kind of people, who were too lazy to work and believed that they should be given the means of living by the people who did work. These lazy people were like the ticks and lice that live on the back of a moose in the spring of the year.

"The lazy people were a source of annoyance to both the greedy people and the well-working people. In time, they affected many of the other two kinds of people. The more machines and wonder-working things were made, the less the ordinary people had to work. Without work to keep them busy, they began to do more and more things that brought harm to the minds of the people themselves and that, in turn, led to their doing harm to other people, and, more and more, they wandered away from the paths that the Great Spirit wanted them to follow.

"In time, these people to whom the Great Spirit had been so kind, in making life easy for them, waged war against groups of people living in other parts of the world and they even went to war among themselves. All this so displeased the Great Spirit that, in disgust, He decided to start all over again with another breed of people, just as a man making a canoe would do if he found the material he was working with was too decayed or too weak to serve his purpose. He would discard what he had done and would begin again with other and better material in the hope that it would prove to be the strong and lasting material he desired. Therefore, the Great Spirit destroyed the people who had failed Him, and began to build a new race of people. Only the few island people who were far away on their big canoes survived the destruction of the island.

"Still another tradition says that the ancient people had many man-made things by means of which many wonderful things could be caused to happen. Soon some evil-minded men began to tell the others that they had so many wonderful things and so many powers that they were even greater than the Great Spirit, and that there was no need to follow what they had been told by the old people were the wishes, orders, or commands of the Great Spirit.

"In a quarrel with other men, they insulted the Great Spirit by drawing down power from the sun and using it against other people. The story tellers did not know what actually happened but, according to their story, several large-canoe loads of men and women were returning home from voyages to other parts of the world. They saw in the distance a great mushroom with flashing lights standing in the ocean over the place where their homeland had been. Then came darkness of night and winds and rain. When daylight returned, no sign of land could be seen; nothing was to be seen but water. All the people of the great island had perished. Only the people in the big canoes far from the island had survived. They scattered in all directions away from the site of their former homeland. Those who were our ancestors came, at last, to dry land, where they had to start to rebuild a new nation, with nothing but stones as tools and with half of their number being unable to see because of their having looked at the bright lights in the giant mushroom.

"Perhaps there have been several great catastrophes or disasters and perhaps the stories about them have become mixed. We know that the stories or traditions have been told and re-told so often that nobody now knows just how much truth may have been in them, to start with, or how much any such truth may have been distorted by contacts with people telling different stories, just as our language has been distorted and changed by branches of our people who did not follow the Great Spirit's orders always to speak precisely and properly the language which the Great Spirit had prepared for us.

"The people who neglected to follow the orders of the Great Spirit, either from laziness, indolence, or from borrowing words or speech habits of other races of men with whom they came in contact in their new world, soon developed dialects or languages so different from our original tongue that in some cases it is difficult to understand what they are saying. Even the language we speak now has had some small changes since our people came to this land, but we have tried harder than any of the other tribes to speak the old language correctly. To remind us of that, we refer to our language as the Nehiyâwewin—the precisely spoken language—and we call ourselves *The Precisely Speaking People*.[7] However, some of our neighbors call us by a name which is a corruption of an older name, Ka-nistum-itlin-ioo-uk, meaning 'They who were the first people.' The white men have shortened that long name to *Knistinoos*."

"I thank you, my grandfather, for telling me all this," said the boy politely. "Do you think that a system of writing our language would be of any value to us?"

"Yes, indeed. I think that it would be a very valuable thing to be able to keep records of things that happen and have happened. We could then place on record, for all people to see, now and in years to come, the stories, tales, and traditions, that are now passed down only from mouth to ear, about things that are believed to have happened in the past."

"I wish I could discover the secret hidden in your Golden Talisman," said the boy wistfully. "Do you have anything else that once belonged to our people before the great disaster?"

"We have this one thing only," replied the old man, "and I have no means of knowing when or where it was made. It is something that has been handed down from father to son to me. When I leave here to journey to the Happy Hunting Grounds, I shall leave it to you. While I am alive and well, however, I must always keep it close to me. Such are the commands passed down to me by my father; and to my father from his father."

The old man then showed the boy his talisman, amulet or charm, which he carried in a small leather bag on a thong around his neck. "You can see, my grandson, this is made not of copper but of pure rustless metal known as gold. It appears to be only part of something it once was. In what appears to have been the central part there is a strong design cut or engraved in the metal. Along the side are some designs or pictures of something unknown to me except that tradition says that the markings Ρ Ր L ᓂ ᗡ represent THE GREAT SPIRIT, but in what way I do not know. This talisman has been handed down through so many generations that no person knows who made it or how it came into the hands of our ancestors.

"Perhaps when you go to the Sacred Hill next moon, to fast and pray for guidance from the Great Spirit, Powakun, the dream spirit, may be sent to reveal to you the secret of the strange markings on the talisman. It is certain to me that these markings have something to do with the ancient system of writing. Now," said the grandfather, "let us think about what you must do before you can become a man. Let us prepare for your journey to the Sacred Hill and for the things you must remember to do there.

"This is the end of the First Book written by me, Peyo-wah-mit, grandson of Moosoom."

8
THE LOST ART OF
WRITING IS RESTORED

On the following morning, they opened another book written, in the syllabic symbols, by Peyo-wah-mit and marked as his second book.

Sandy could understand the spoken language, except for unusual terms or phrases, but, of course, could not read the written language.

Kesee Pay and his daughter Papeet, in turn, read aloud from the book, pausing now and then to explain unusual terms to Sandy.

When translated into modern English, what they read aloud to him would appear as follows:

The Second Book of Peyo-Wah-Mit Telling How the Dream Spirit Taught Him to Write

After the boy, Peyo-wah-mit, had been shown the Golden Talisman by his grandfather, he became more and more interested in the possibility of there being a system of writing for his nation's language. He studied carefully the strange markings on the talisman, but he could not understand how they could have any connection with the words of the spoken language of his people.

He knew that when boys reached his age they went through certain ceremonial rites before they could be accepted as "men" by the older persons of his tribe. He knew that one of these rites involved a visit to the Sacred Hill, where the boy must remain alone, without food or water, until he would be visited by a dream spirit who would talk with him and would give him information and advice on the conduct of his life to come.

Peyo-wah-mit's grandfather had said that it was time for him to go to the Sacred Hill, so the boy became determined to ask the dream spirit about his grandfather's gold talisman and to ask that he might be taught how to write his own spoken language. He said nothing about this to his grandfather but listened intently to all the information and advice given to him by the older man.

In the days that followed, the boy was given instructions on how he was to prepare for the fasting ordeal each boy of his age had to undergo before he could be qualified to take his place as a man of his tribe.

The Sacred Hill was in a desolate place that was never visited except by persons desiring to communicate with, or rather, desiring communication from, the Great Spirit. When a person was known to be in the cavern on the eastern side of the hill, near the top, no other person would attempt to go near it, from fear of the "bad medicine" that might come to him for interfering with the work of the Great Spirit.

The boy was told how he must take a complete change of clean clothing, and food for his return journey. The food was to be left at the foot of the hill and must not be touched until after he had seen the Dream Spirit. While at the cave near the top of the hill, he must neither eat nor drink until the dream-vision came to him. If he should be too weak to resist the temptation to eat or drink, it would mean that he was not yet fit to be called a man, and he must return home at once and wait until he was "man enough" to try again. He was to take with him to the cave only a small stone jar of water which he must not touch until after he had seen the dream-vision. Only after he had seen the vision could he drink the water. This would give him strength to reach the food left at the foot of the hill, which, in turn, would give him strength to return to his home. This was considered necessary because with some boys it took many days and nights of fasting before the dream-vision came to them.

The boy, Peyo-wah-mit, was told that near the entrance to the cavern near the top of the hill he would find many pieces of slate rock; thin flat layers of soft gray stone with smooth surfaces on which pictures could be scratched with a sharp corner of another kind of very hard white rock to be found mixed with the pieces of slate. He was told that he should take three pieces of the white rock and three larger sheets of the slate rock, and to keep them near him

57

in the cave. This was so that he could scratch on the slate any signs or marks revealed to him in the course of the dream-vision.

In due course the boy approached the Sacred Hill. He bathed in the stream near the foot of the hill and he adorned himself in his best and cleanest clothes; breechclout, leggings, moccasins, and a decorated buckskin robe over his shoulders. He had already built a mound of rocks over the small stock of food he had brought to give him strength for the return journey to his home after the fasting ordeal.

He selected three pieces of smooth slate and three pieces of the sharp-cornered white rock as he climbed to the mouth of the cave near the top of the hill. He gathered branches of trees and brush with which he made a bed. He placed the jar of water where he could not see it. He began to pray to the Great Spirit to send the dream spirit to tell him what he must do to be a man worthy of his grandfather and his tribe.

Two long days and two long nights went by, but no dream spirit appeared. The temptation to take just one little sip of water was almost overpowering; just one little sip, who would ever know? "No," said the boy to himself, "I would know, and for the rest of my life it would haunt me to know that I had been such a coward."

On the third night after beginning his prayers to the Great Spirit asking that the dream spirit be sent to him, the boy was aroused from sleep by feeling a hand on his shoulder shaking him gently. He sat up in what appeared to be broad daylight, but in a very strange structure such as he had never seen before.

In front of him was a beautiful woman who appeared to be perhaps fifteen or twenty years older than he was. She was dressed quite differently from the women of his race; in materials different from anything he had ever seen. And what particularly amazed him was the fact that her long hair was not straight and jet black like that of women he had seen but was wavy and the color of polished copper.

He was so amazed to see a woman, instead of the man that he had expected to see, that he was speechless. The woman laughed softly and said assuringly, "Do not look so astonished, my young friend. Did you think that only men are the dream-vision servants of the Great Spirit? You will learn that ideas about the relative positions of men and women change with the times. In the age in which you live, and in the section of the earth in which your people live, men may appear to be the important sex, but it has not always been so, and it will not always be so. What did you most desire from the dream spirit you asked the Great Spirit to send to you?"

At last, the boy found his voice. "I desired to be advised how to become a man worthy of my tribe; a man of physical strength and mental intelligence and, most of all, a man of wisdom; a man that my grandfather and men like him could always be proud of."

"Was that all you desired?" asked the woman.

"No," admitted the boy slowly, "I had hoped I might be told how I could help my fellow men by bringing to them a system of writing our language. I had hoped that the dream spirit would help me to think of some way my people could be enabled to write in their own language as the white men, so I have been told, write in their language. I wish you were able to help me with this," he added in a disappointed tone.

"Cheer up, young man," said the woman softly, "your wish may be granted. I am here because the Great Spirit has listened to your prayers. I have been sent to show you how your language may be written. So, sit at ease, and please listen to me.

"Many thousands of moons ago your people—The Precisely Speaking People—had a written language, or a system for writing their spoken language, which had been used by their ancestors in another world, far out in the sky, before they came to live in this world you know. But because of the last great catastrophe which happened to this world and to most of the old races of human beings on it, the art of writing the language was lost to your ancestors. If the Great Spirit decides in your favor, you may be the man through whose efforts your people may recover their lost art of writing. I am to tell you first about the written language and, later, something of the history of your people so that you may record it for the information of your people and for mankind in general who will learn from them.

"I want you to pay careful attention to all that I am going to tell you and show you because you will not only pass the information to your people but will enable other persons in the future to read the many historical and technical records stored carefully by your ancestors and still in good condition in places now unknown to mankind. The locations and the means of recovery of those records will be revealed eventually and, through the help of your writings, will be read and understood, but it may be many many years before all those records will be found.

"I shall go into a lot of what may seem to you to be tiresome detail about the syllabic system of writing but it is essential that you know the basic principles of it, because this information is not only for the use of your people in the not too distant future but is for the information of future generations of mankind of various races and languages.

"Long before the last great catastrophe that caused so much destruction to the world on which you live, the wise men of the ancient red-haired race recorded in many books, and other means of making permanent records, vast amounts of historical and techical information, and carefully stored them in places which they thought would be secure from destruction or damage, even if such storage places might be buried deeply in mud carried by raging torrents of water produced by an upset world spinning wildly for a time, as they knew had happened before.

"Some of those records were in books that had pages of thin metal that would not be affected by age. Other books had pages of very thin ice-like material that could bend without breaking or cracking and would remain readable over untold ages. Two systems of writing were used. One was for the language of your ancestors, which had relatively few sounds, and one was suitable for use in recording it and some other languages that contained some sounds not used in the language of the old red-haired race.

"It is the syllabic system of your ancestors that I will now demonstrate to you.

She pointed to one of the tablets of slate rock that the boy had selected before he began his fast. "Hand me that tablet and a piece of the white rock for making marks on it."

The boy did so, and the woman continued, "First I shall show you the key to the system of writing. Look at these marks."

With a sharp corner of the hard white rock she scratched on the softer slate rock the following four designs: ⊐ ⊔ ⊓ ⊏

"These three-sided figures represent different sounds all beginning with the sound of T in your language, one of the most important sounds in the language because, according to its use, it can mean everything or nothing. You can not pronounce the sound without moving your tongue, but there are sounds in your language

60

which you can make without moving the tip of your tongue, and without moving your open lips. These sounds are: oo, ay, ee, ah. They are called vowels or vowel sounds. These four vowel sounds (sometimes long and sometimes short) can be combined with many sounds that do require the use of the tongue or the lips. The latter sounds are called consonants. A consonant combined with a following vowel is called a syllable. Any mark designed and used to represent the sound of a syllable can be called a syllabic symbol or a 'syllabic.'

"Your language and the languages of many other people can be written by using syllabic symbols to represent the sounds of syllables of the language concerned. The four marks   ⅃ ⊔ ⊓ ⊏ are syllabic symbols. Each one represents the sound of one certain syllable. In the order in which they are shown they represent the sounds of: too, tay, tee, tah.

"Notice what happens when we draw them in a group with the second two under the first two: ⅃⊔
⊓⊏

"If we let the adjoining double lines overlap to form one line, we have the figure: ╂   . This is called a 'cross,' and it is symbolic of the spiritual side of humanity and mankind's relationship with the Great Spirit. The figures or markings used for writing are symbols for certain sounds."

She then showed him the symbols for each syllabic sound of their language, and he copied them on thin plates of slate rock. She showed him how all the syllabic symbols were combined in one basic design which she drew carefully on a piece of slate and told him to guard it most carefully and to copy it many times so that he would always remember it.

This was the design:

She then continued her instructions.

"The symbols I have shown you were used when writing was chiselled on stone or metal, because straight lines were easier to make than were curved lines, but when writing was done on parchment, paper, leather, or on thin sheets of hammered gold, curves were easier to make and certain syllabic symbols were changed from straight line form to partly curved form; thus:

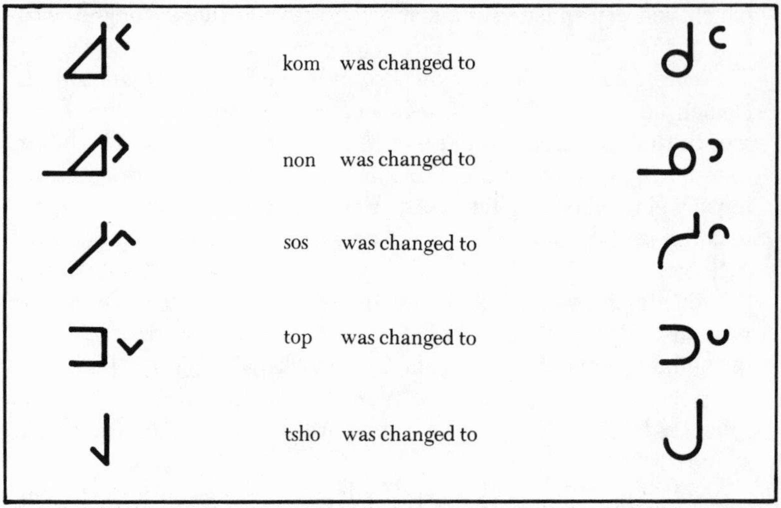
kom was changed to
non was changed to
sos was changed to
top was changed to
tsho was changed to

"A dot placed to the right of any syllabic symbol indicates that the sound of w comes immediately *before* the vowel sound. Thus, ᐅ represents the sound of o, but ᐅᐧ represents the sound of wo, and while ᑫ represents the sound of kay, the dot placed after it, like this, ᑫᐧ makes it represent the sound of kway.

"When a dot is placed *over* a syllabic symbol, it indicates that the sound of the vowel is 'long.' The sound of h before a vowel is indicated by the mark ′ before the symbol for the vowel sound. When there is a sudden short pause *after* a vowel sound, this is indicated by the marks ″ placed after the the symbol containing the vowel. Final oo is represented by o .

"I will now write on your tablet of stone the syllabic symbols used in writing your language. Watch carefully how I make them. On each line I will show a short word that begins with the first syllabic symbol on that line."

When the dream spirit was satisfied that the boy understood the principles of the syllabic system of writing his languge, and had a record of the symbols, she said to him:

"You must now cease your fasting and return to your grandfather. Repeat to him all I have told you. You must then study the syllabic symbols and learn to use them. You must continually practice writ-

ᐅ ᐊ ᐁ ᐃ	oyakan	ᐅᔮᑲᐣ	a dish
ᔪ ᔭ ᔦ ᔨ -	yotin	ᔫᑎᐣ	the wind
ᑯ ᑲ ᑫ ᑭ `	kona	ᑯᓈ	snow
ᒧ ᒪ ᒣ ᒥ ᒼ	moostoos	ᒨᐢᑑᐢ	a buffalo
ᓄ ᓇ ᓀ ᓂ ᐣ	nokwan	ᓄᑳᐧᐣ	it is visible
ᐳ ᐸ ᐯ ᐱ ᑊ	ponepuyoo	ᐳᓂᐸᔫ	it ceases
ᓱ ᓴ ᓭ ᓯ ᐢ	sokesioo	ᓱᑮᓯᐤ	he is strong
ᑐ ᑕ ᑌ ᑎ ᐟ	totum	ᑐᑕᒼ	he does it
ᒍ ᒐ ᒉ ᒋ -	tshookupāyoo	ᒎᑲᐯᔫ	the man in the moon

ing; and reading what you have written. Your grandfather will show you how to make black liquid and how to mark with it on birch bark.

"At the time of the fifth full moon from now, if you are still interested in the system of writing your language, you are to come back here, and I shall tell you about things that happened to your people long ago. You must go to sleep now and rest. When you wake you will take a small drink of water from your water jug. Soon after that the sun will rise and you will eat of the food you brought with you. Then you must begin the journey back to the home of your grandfather."

The boy did as he was told to do. With great care he carried the slate tablet to his grandfather, and showed it to him, and repeated to him all the words of the dream spirit.

"Behold, my grandfather," said the boy eagerly, "the Golden Talisman that you have is a wonderful thing. It shows half of the design that was shown to me by the dream spirit as the key to the written language of the ancients. It must be something that was once the property of the ancient people. But why was it cut in half? Where do you suppose is the other half of it?"

"Perhaps," replied his grandfather, "your dream spirit will tell you, when you go back to see her. Now, I will show you how to make the black liquid, or ink, and a painting stick, or pen, from the quill of a goose feather, so that you can begin learning how to write our language. You must work diligently because the time will pass very rapidly until you go back to the Sacred Hill."

"This is the end of the second book written by me; Peyo-wah-mit, grandson of Moosoom."

9
WHY BOOKS OF INFORMATION WERE HIDDEN

The medicine man and his daughter did their best in trying to explain to Sandy the details of the strange system of writing. He began to realize that if a person practiced enough he or she would find that reading the syllabic symbols would become as easy as reading the printed letters of any other language, and they did not require as many letters as did the English language.

Sandy was told that the other book in the possession of Kesee Pay was different from the others in that it dealt chiefly with things that happened after he had obtained the paper books and was able to record many things told to him by the dream spirit and, in particular, it explained why and how other very important books were to be hidden for the information of future generations.

On the following day Papeet began to read the book aloud.

The Eighth Book of Peyo-Wah-Mit

After my second meeting with the dream spirit, I returned to the home of my grandfather and tried faithfully to carry out the instructions of the dream spirit. During the winter that followed, I collected and prepared many sheets of birch bark on which I wrote down all the things told to me at the Sacred Hill. I was not satisfied with the sheets of birch bark because they had the tendency to curl, and to split, and to tear. Also, I was afraid they might not keep well and might crumble into powder after a few years.

During the winter, my grandfather was visited by men from an eastern tribe who told him that a white man had set up a trading store near their village at the eastern end of the great fresh water lake, Kitshe Kumee, and that he had several books of sheets of blank paper on which he wrote records of his business transactions each day, and on which he made drawings of many things.

I wished that I could have such blank paper on which I might write, instead of using the birch bark. I believed that the paper would be easier to write on and would be much more permanent.

After much discussion with my grandfather, it was decided that I could go, with four experienced canoe men, to the eastern end of Kitshe Kumee where resided the white trader who might have the books I desired.

After the ice went out in the spring, we made the long journey to the shore of Kitshe Kumee and then along the northern shore of that great body of water to the rapids where the waters of that great lake rush down into another lake, and in due course we arrived at the village.

We found friendly people in the village but we were told that the trader was absent, having gone eastward for a fresh stock of supplies for his trading post. It was expected, however, that he should return within half a moon.

We were told that there was a party of white men encamped half a days paddling distance to the southward from the village. These white men were reported to be intending to explore the great lake which extended far to the south of Kitshee Kumee and they were overhauling their canoes while one of their men, who was dressed in long black robes was spending all his time talking to the natives in their own language; or in a half understandable corruption of their language. He was telling them that everything they believed about the Great Spirit was wrong and that they must believe only what he told them.

I wished to see and hear this man. First of all, I hoped he might have a blank book he might give me in exchange for some fine furs we had brought with us. Secondly, I wished to hear what he had to say. We went to see him and were given what appeared to be a friendly reception. The black robed praying man was a constant talker but at times it was difficult to understand what he was trying to say, because many of his sentences were made up of words in the wrong order as if he had many things backwards in his mind. The language he spoke was not our language but was some badly corrupted dialect sufficiently near it in many words that by listening carefully and guessing at half of the missing or unknown words we were able to get a fair understanding of what he was trying to say. The local men who accompanied us from the village at the rapids understood him much better than we did and later they explained to us all the things they thought he said.

One of the men from the village who came with us to visit the praying man was a local chief and a very serious thinker. I had shown him the copper plate that I carried. This was the plate I had made according to the instructions given to me by the dream spirit. It showed the symbols used in writing our language. I also showed to the chief a roll of birch bark I carried, on which I had written various details of what we had seen on our journey from my home to his village. He was intensely interested in the systems of writing and was beginning to get a fair understanding of it when we arrived at the camp of the white praying-man.

I told the chief that I intended to show the praying-man my copper plate with the writing symbols on it. The chief told me I might regret doing so too soon. He counseled me that white men were very different from our people in their behaviour and that they were not to be trusted to do the things that our people would do under similar circumstances. Often they spoke with false tongues and would say one thing but mean something else. He advised me not to let the praying-man know anything about the "new system of writing" until I knew more about him and his actions. I asked the chief what harm could be done by telling the praying-man about our system of writing and how it had been given to me by the dream spirit. I said it might help to influence him to give me a blank book in which I could write the things told to me by the dream spirit.

The chief said to me that what little he had learned about white praying-men led him to believe that they were not sensible like ordinary men and it was impossible to predict what they might do next—except to talk, talk, talk. He said that they seldom really listened to anything except their own words and their echoes, and they did so many crazy things that he would not trust one with anything of value. He told me not to show the copper plate to the praying-man until I could be sure he would not keep the plate and steal the system of writing for himself and the use of the white men.

Being young and inexperienced with white men, and being headstrong in my interest in the writing system, I did everything wrongly. All too soon, I showed the praying-man my roll of birch bark and explained to him the general idea of the system of writing. He appeared to be very interested in it. He said to me, "This is wonderful, my son. You must tell me all about it and how you came to learn about it."

I said that it had been shown to me by the dream spirit. With that, he became very friendly in attitude and said with a beaming smile, "My son, my son, you must tell me all about the dream spirit and I shall do all I can to help you. Perhaps, only perhaps, I may be able to spare you a blank book of paper, but first you must tell me your story."

Feeling that I was talking with a friend, I told him about my meeting with the dream spirit and I showed him the copper plate and the symbols used in writing.

The praying-man asked me if I had any more birch bark with writing thereon. I tried to understand his badly mangled attempt to speak our language and, as I understood him, he asked if I had any other writings on birch bark *there* with me at the time, but I now think he was asking if I had any other writing *anywhere*. At any rate, I told him that I had no writing other than the roll of birch bark I showed him—meaning that I had no other writing *there*.

I was about to tell him some of the things the dream spirit had told me but suddenly he jumped up from where we had been sitting and shouted to the other white men, and to the natives who were in the vicinity, to come with him to the shore of the lake where he had something to tell them all.

He was holding in his hand my copper plate with the writing symbols on it. He was waving this in the air over his head so all could see it. He instructed two white men to start a small fire in front of him. When it was burning briskly he began to speak.

"I command you all to listen to me and to rejoice with me in that I have saved this young man," pointing his finger at me, "from the Evil Spirit. This young man's mind has become possessed of the Evil Spirit who taught him the Evil Spirit's own system of writing your heathen language. If he were to be permitted to use this writing to record all your heathenish and pagan and sinful beliefs and traditions it would be war against the true religion which I am bringing to you. The Evil Spirit knew I was coming so he set up this war against me and my religion so that you might have your own evil books of heathen writing in opposition to my true Holy Writings.

Therefore, as a true soldier of the Cross, I begin the battle by destroying this work of the Evil Spirit, just as the noble Father Landa did with the evil writings he found in the new world of Spanish America. I throw this evil piece of metal into the deep waters of the lake, where it will be seen no more and I give this evil roll of birch bark to the flames of this fire, for the destruction it so rightly deserves."

As he spoke, to the astonishment of all, he threw my roll of writing into the fire and he hurled my copper plate far out into the lake before I or anyone else could think of stopping him.

He then turned on me like an angry, crazy man and said many things of which only a few sentences could be remembered exactly by me or my friends. Discussing his outburst with others and piecing together what we had heard him say, we agreed that he had declared that I was an evil heathen and should be shunned by all men because my mind and body had become possessed by an evil spirit who was trying to teach them evil and to lead them farther away from the truth which he brought to us in his Book. He threw his head back and looked toward the sky and spoke as if talking to some unseen person in the sky, saying:

". . . This day brings great joy to my heart, because to me has been given the great honour of nipping in the bud the heathenish conspiracy of the Evil Spirit to lead all the red-skinned people astray by producing a method of writing whereby all the evil beliefs, traditions and stories of false gods and false tales of evil things could be recorded and read and thereby kept alive in the minds of all these people and their children and their children's children instead of being forgotten as they should be.

"Great must be the joy among all the saints in heaven this day for what I have done to save so many souls yet unborn from the everlasting damnation in the eternal flames that would have been their fate if the evil book of false beliefs and pagan stories had been permitted to be written. Now it is finished. The system of writing invented by the Evil Spirit has been destroyed and my prayer is 'that the mind of this young instrument of the Evil Spirit will become blank and all memories of the evil writings will be removed from it' and that the whole idea of the writing may be forgotten by all who ever heard of it."

From that moment onward, the white men acted as if I were

some evil thing they could not get rid of fast enough. We were told to leave their camp ground at once. We were very glad to do so.

I was astonished and bewildered at the actions of the white praying-man, and so were my companions, especially the chief, who had, himself, shown so much interest in the written language. We could not understand why a man who appeared to be so friendly and so helpfully interested in my desire to write in my own language, would so suddenly become a raving maniac and would take it into his own hands to destroy things that did not belong to him and which he knew I considered to be things of value to me and to my people. No sane man of the Nayheyawayoo people would ever act in such an unmanly manner.

As we began to paddle away from the shore, the chief asked me if his men, who were good swimmers, should try to recover the copper plate from the bottom of the lake. I said, "Yes, by all means, if you think it can be done." I said this without thinking that the white men on the shore might try to prevent us. As we turned toward the place where the plate had entered the water, the praying-man evidently guessed our intentions and he shouted:

"Keep moving or my men will shoot!" A few seconds later a gun was fired and a bullet hit the water only two or three canoe lenths ahead of our foremost canoe. We did not linger but the chief ordered each of his men to mark well and remember where the copper plate had disappeared. I assumed that he intended to return at some more opportune time and to attempt to recover the plate.

When we arrived at the village near the stream of rapid water connecting the two great lakes, we found that the white trader had arrived with a brigade of canoes carrying his trade goods. He wanted our furs. I told him about my desire to obtain blank books of paper.

He told me that he had a few such books which he used for keeping his own records of sales, debts, and so on, but could not understand why I should desire to possess such books when I could not possibly know how to write in them. I said that I could at least draw pictures in them—having learned a lesson from the praying-man, I did not tell him about the system of writing our language. At least, I did not tell him about it at first, but, after he had accepted half our prime furs for a mere four books of blank paper, I told him about our experience with the praying-man of his race.

At first he seemed to be afraid of something and wanted his books back, but when we refused to trade him any more of our furs in exchange for the trade goods he wanted us to take, he changed his mind and said:

"I am sure that his self-styled holiness, Father Osumitonayoo, will come to me and will ask me if I have supplied you with any paper. If I tell him, yes, he will cause much trouble for me. If I tell him, no, he will order me to confess my sins to him. If I then go to him on bended knee in confession and tell him that not one little scrap of paper did you get from me, he will go away happy and will leave me in peace, and what he doesn't know will not cause me to lose any sleep on earth, or cause me to spend any extra time in the place midway between earth and heaven. All I ask of you is that you tell no man of this place that I supplied books of paper to you. The local chief and his people must not be told. Only you and I are to know anything about the books. Only on this condition will I let you depart with the books. I believe that you are an honorable man and will keep your promise, if made."

I promised that until I returned to my grandfather I would tell no man where or from whom I obtained my books. At that we parted as friends and after exchanging the remainder of our furs for trade goods we started our journey homeward amid his cries to return with more fur and to bring others with furs to trade.

Our return journey was uneventful. After my arrival at my home I told my grandfather about our experiences and then I began to write in the books of paper.

After I had written the story of my second meeting with the dream spirit, I read the whole of it aloud to my grandfather and my sister. They were amazed that so many words could be recorded in one small book and, of course, they were very interested in the things that had been told to me by the dream spirit. My grandfather, in particular, was interested not only in the things I had written but he was worried, a little, that perhaps I had written things in a way they might appear to have meaning different from the meaning intended by the dream spirit. He thought that it would be best to try to communicate once more with the dream spirit and to read to her what I had written in the book, so that she might correct any possible errors I might have made.

It was decided that I should return to the Sacred Hill and fast until the dream spirit appeared. This time I was to take the books in which I had written the things she had told me to write.

I was at the proper place on the Sacred Hill for two nights and two days and part of a third night before the strange light appeared in the cave and I looked up and saw the dream spirit beside me. I jumped up but she held up her hand and told me to be seated. She then sat down beside me and said, "You have done well, Niseem." The word Niseem means 'my younger brother' and this was the first time that she had used this term of relationship. Coming from her, it was a great honor to be so addressed.

"You have done well," she repeated. "You have succeeded in procuring books in which to write the things I told you to write and you have written those things. Now, I would like you to read to me all that you have written."

I read to her. Now and then she would bid me to pause while she pointed out some changes that I should make, or where words or sentences should be added. This took considerable time but at last this checking of my written work was completed.

Strange as it appeared to me at the time, she did not ask me about the events that had taken place when I talked with the black-robed praying-man, but she began to talk to me as if she knew all about what had happened.

I asked her if she considered me at fault for letting the white praying-man have the opportunity to destroy the copper plate on which was engraved the syllabic writing symbols of our language.

"Who am I to say you were at fault, my younger brother?" she replied. "What has been done has been done. We all do things that seem to be perfectly logical and correct at the time but which turn out later to have been mistakes or unfortunate actions. We are never alone in anything we do. We are only one of many factors involved in anything we may do. We seldom, if ever, have control of those other factors. Perhaps we do the right thing but because of the existence of other factors unknown to us, the end result is quite different from what we expected. Perhaps we do the wrong thing but, in spite of that, the other factors involved may be such that the end result is what was intended. All through life, each one of us, human being or Experimenter, is progressing through a network of paths of influence. What happens depends upon which of the branching and intersecting paths we happen to follow and which of those paths we do not follow—and how long we follow any path before branching off on another.

"So long as you follow what your own conscience believes to be the correct path, you are doing the right thing. One must always keep on friendly terms with one's conscience and consult it on points for and against any action.

"In your meeting with the black-robed praying-man, you had no reason to suspect that he would try to destroy your roll of inscribed bark or your copper plate, and, therefore, no fault can be charged to you. Now that what happened has happened, I can tell you that the time is not yet ripe for white men to be given the system of writing your language. The paths of fate have been interfered with by the fanatical bigotry of the black-robed white man, and before the paths will again be in position for another attempt to have the system of writing returned to your people, as a whole, the moon in the sky must wax and wane twenty-four hundred times. You will not live to see that day but you will teach the system of writing to your heir and your heir must teach it to his or her children, and so on with each succeeding generation. As I have said, it can not be revived and brought to the common use of your people for approximately another two hundred years, although, if all goes well, some of your descendants will make good use of it in less than half that time.

"Your friend, the chief at the village beyond the far end of Kitshe Kumee, has already recovered the copper plate from the bottom of the lake and he has been instructed to protect it from corroding by keeping it coated with grease, and he is to instruct his descendants to keep it as a secret sacred relic until the time comes for the arrival of a white praying man, not of the black robe religion, who will be known to them as 'Brother Tshim.'

"The logical paths of fate are such that if properly followed, this Brother Tshim will be shown the copper plate and he will immediately understand the importance of the use of this system for making known, to your people, the Holy Scriptures and instructions of his religion. He will propose to his superiors that the writing system be adopted for use. They will reject his recommendations and fifty more moons will wax and wane before he succeeds in having the system of writing put into practical use and taught to your people. It will then be known to the white men as his personal invention—

not because Brother Tshim[8] will claim it to be so, but because he will be the one to put it into practical use."

The dream spirit continued, "You are to learn from your grandfather all the arts and skills he knows as a medicine man. These are to be practiced and passed on to successors by you and your heirs and successors. I have told you something of inherited memories. There is something else I shall tell you. It is possible for some persons to be assisted in recalling his or her inherited memories, by being put into a controlled sleep or hypnotic trance. I shall teach you how this may be done and you are to teach it to your successor of the next generation, and this is to be passed on from one generation of your descendants to another. But remember well, if any one of these persons, including yourself, should ever use these powers to do harm to anyone, or should he ever use them for personal gain or reward to the detriment of any other person, the powers will be taken away from him. He will know if he has broken the rule and will simply be unable to control the person whose memories he wishes to be recalled.

"The procedure to be followed in inducing the controlled sleep or hypnotic trance is not to be written. It must be passed on by word of mouth only. This is very important. It must not be described in writing and it must not be given to any person other than a qualified and recognized medicine man or medicine woman."

The dream spirit then told me certain things I must do after I returned to the home of my grandfather. First of all, I was to complete the work of recording the events and the information and instructions received by me at all three meetings with the dream spirit. Everything I could remember was to be written down with the exception of one thing—how to recall inherited memories of another person.

When the writing would be completed I was to place the books, including a copy of this book, carefully wrapped, in an airtight container disguised to look like a boulder of rock, and I was to hide it in a pile of similar looking rocks in a certain part of the secret cave in the Sacred Hill.

The dream spirit told me how a clay container and cover could be made and how it could be baked hard in the fire. After it had cooled, the books would be placed inside. She told me how to burn certain different kinds of rock until they could easily be pounded

74

into powder. These powders were to be mixed together with sand and when water was added to the mixture a muddy material would result that, when allowed to dry slowly, would look like and would become as hard and strong as solid rock. While still in the state of thick mud it was to be daubed all over the clay container and shaped to resemble a boulder of stone.

The dream spirit also told me that I must inform my heir, who in turn must inform his heir, that "The hidden books are not to be removed from their hiding place until the other half of the sacred talisman comes to join the half which your grandfather now has in his possession. When that time comes, the holder of your grandfather's half of the talisman will be guided to do what is right in uncovering the books and in making known their contents to the proper persons."

The dream spirit asked me to repeat to her all the things she had told me to do. She listened and then ordered me to write the things that were to be written. I did so, and then read to her what I had written. She agreed that I had written correctly. She then taught me the secrets of the hypnotic sleep. It seemed like days before she had completed her instructions. When she was satisfied with my reaction to her instructions, she told me that this would be the end of our talks at this time. Suddenly, she disappeared as mysteriously as she had appeared. When the light of her presence went out I must have fallen exhausted into sleep.

When I awoke, the sun was shining into the mouth of the cave. After eating and drinking and resting long enough for my strength of body to return, I began the journey back to my grandfather's home.

Time has now passed and we have completed the construction of the container for the books. When we have put the carefully wrapped books inside and have sealed it, and the muddy covering has dried, it will be wrapped in skins so that no man will know just what is being carried suspended from the pole resting on the shoulders of two strong men who will go with me to the foot of the Sacred Hill. The two men will return and I shall carry the container to the hiding place and conceal it there.

May the Great Spirit bless and guide the next reader of this, the eighth book written by me.

Peyo-wah-mit, grandson of Moosoom.

10
INHERITED MEMORIES
EXPLAINED

After Papeet finished reading the books written by Peyo-wah-mit, Sandy and her father spent a long time discussing the various strange happenings reported by the author of the books.

Sandy was interested in what had been written about the thing that was not to be described in writing because knowledge of it was to be passed on only verbally.

"Can you tell me," he asked Kesee Pay, "anything about what your grandfather meant about 'inherited memories'? I am not sure just what is meant by that term."

"The dream spirit taught my grandfather," replied Kesee Pay, "and he taught me, not only what is meant by 'inherited memories' but how to activate those memories in the head of a person so that they can be recalled.

"According to what I have been taught, each one of us has two kinds of memories: living memory and inherited memory. The living memory is the system of memories of things that affected our senses of sight, sound, and thinking from the time we were very young children to the present time. This is really a wonderous thing, but such a common thing and so constantly in use that we take it for granted and never really think how wonderful it is that we can, just by merely thinking about it, recall a scene, sounds, or thoughts that actually happened many years ago or as recently as a few minutes ago.

"Sometimes, even, we may see a stranger and have the feeling 'where have I seen this person before?' or we may hear something and feel certain that we have heard the same thing before.

"Some people used to believe that they had lived other lives, or that the spirits of men and women were reborn over and over in different bodies in different generations. That does not happen.

"What really happens is that sometimes we have a flash of memory from another life, but that does *not* mean that we ever lived before. It does mean that when each of us is born we bring into the world with us a very faint copy of what was the living memory of each of our ancestors. These are *inherited memories*.

"It is impossible for us to imagine how so much can be carried in the seed germ of a human being, but the Great Spirit knows no limit to the size of small things as well as no limit to the size of large things. We do not know how it happens. We only know that it does happen. In the head of each one of us is a copy of what once was the living memory of each and every one of our ancestors. Thus, in your head you have not only your own living memory which you can call upon at will but you have a copy of the complete memory of your father's father from the time when he was a child until he begat your father—but you have nothing from the memory of your father's father *after* he passed on what he remembered at the time when he begat your father.

"When your father begat you, he passed on to you a copy of his own living memory and a copy of the inherited memory which *his* father had passed on to him. Your father's memory might include *his* memories of his father's life after he begat your father but your father would have no inherited memories from his father after that event.

"Each one of us human beings was brought into this world by two persons, a father and a mother, and we can inherit memories from each of them.

"Each of our two parents had two parents; therefore, each of them received two lots of inherited memories from each of their parents, and so on with each generation. As we go back in time, we find that for every generation the load of copies of inherited memories was doubled for each and every person involved. This would be in the order of 1, 2, 4, 8, 16, 32, 64, 128, 256, 512, etc., going back generation after generation.

"Now, let us assume that there is a period of twenty-five years between the birth of one man and the time when he begets his offspring, male or female.

"Extending back to the time one hundred winters before your own living memory began to function, you then had thirty-two ancestors whose memories you inherited at birth. Going back another hundred years, we find that at the time two hundred years

77

before your birth you had five hundred and twelve ancestors. Add them all together and you will see that in the past two hundred years there were one thousand and twenty-two persons from whom you received copies of their memories—a copy of the memory of each such person from the time he or she began to remember things until the time of conception of the offspring that became another of your ancestors.

"Now, you can see that an awful lot of copies of memories had to be packed into that small egg that was the start of your life. You can also realize why some of those memories may be very faint, and difficult to sort out, and why you can not recall them quickly in the way you can recall memories of events in your own life.

"Your head, my friend, is a storehouse of masses of copies of memories of *parts* of the lives of your ancestors—thousands of them. One mystery of life is how can they be there; another and greater mystery is, 'how can they be activated or recalled by the person carrying that load of inherited memories?'

"We believe that some of our story tellers unconsciously speak and give information from inherited memories when they are supposed to be merely repeating traditions taught to them by some living person. For that reason, we have a motto which says, in effect:

Never believe anything you hear and only half of what you see but never disbelieve anything in its entirety.

. . . meaning that no matter what we may hear there may be some truth in it because of reasons we do not know or can not understand, and real knowledge may have come to the speaker from his inherited memories."

Sandy had listened earnestly to Kesee Pay's explanation of inherited memories and was quick to show his interest in the subject. "This is," he said, "a most interesting subject and your explanation sounds logical and reasonable even if almost unbelievable. It could explain some strange things that have happened in my own life, such as my feeling of having known Papeet somewhere in the past, or someone very, very much like her. I wonder if she and I could have some ancestors in common. Do you think that possible? Do you know how we might find out?"

"There is a way whereby we might find an answer to that,"

declared the medicine man. "I am not sure that it will work satis-factorily but if you are willing to follow my suggestions and will place yourself in my hands for an experiment we might find some information that will help to solve the mystery.

"My grandfather taught me the mysteries of inherited memories and how they could be activated in the minds of some human beings. I say some human beings, for not all human beings are born with minds that have the ability for clear recall of such subcon-scious memories as they may have inherited.

"I am hoping, my red-haired friend, that you will permit me to attempt to recall memories which I suspect you have inherited along with your red hair. I can not do this without your consent and co-operation, but I assured you that no harm should come to you from what I may do. The information which might come from such an experiment might be of value to you and certainly should be of interest to you. Are you willing to co-operate with me?"

"This is all a mystery to me," said Sandy, "but I am willing to do anything within reason that you may desire. Just what is it that you wish me to do?"

"As I said before," replied the medicine man, "I am sure that no harm will come to you. All you have to do is to let me put you to sleep, not normal sleep, but hypnotic sleep, during which time I would talk to you and ask you questions and you would answer those questions from memories stored in your mind and to which you do not have access in your ordinary waking state, unless they have been activated by a skilled person while you are in a state of hypnotic sleep."

Sandy was amazed that such a thing could be done, but he was interested in all mysteries of nature and assured the medicine man that he was willing to play his part. It was arranged that the attempt to obtain information from Sandy's inherited memories would be made on the following day.

11
SANDY'S INHERITED MEMORIES

Sandy was seated near the fire in the center of the lodge but with his right side toward the fire. In front of him the medicine man had placed, on an upturned basket, a crystal of quartz about three inches long. The flickering flames of the fire were reflected from the crystal and Sandy had been told to watch them closely without looking away from the crystal. Papeet was seated nearby, with writing material ready to take notes of what might be said by Sandy if he talked after being put into the expected trance.

The medicine man began to make an incantation, in a low voice. What he said was mostly unintelligible to the big white man but occasionally Sandy caught the words, "Thou art sleepy," "Thine eyelids are heavy," "Close thine eyes and sleep." These sentences were repeated over and over, but mixed in with other words which he could not understand.

It was only a short time before Sandy's head began to nod and a few moments later he was asleep. The medicine man ordered him to lie down, to make himself comfortable, and to answer questions.

The first few questions that were asked by the medicine man were answered partly in the Indian language but partly in a language which the questioner assumed must be the native language of the white man—Gaelic.

The medicine man repeatedly told the hypnotized man, "You know the Indian tongue and you must talk to me only in that tongue. In your mind is a complete record of things that happened in the lives of your ancestors, and a record of the thoughts of your ancestors. They are ideas, regardless of the sounds used to represent those ideas. You can now think back and recall from those stores of memories, the answers to my questions. Just try to think back as if you were trying to recall something in your own past life. Tell me how your ancestors came to be living in the land of your birth. Can you recall anything about that?"

"Yes," said Sandy, in his ordinary voice and speaking in the Indian language, "I can remember when we, men and women, came ashore from the ship and made new homes for ourselves. We intermarried with other people of that land. Then, later, we were fleeing northward from the big-knife men who had invaded our green homeland. They were small men with black hair and sun-tanned faces and spoke a strange language. They were our enemies for many generations, but, in time, they disappeared and were known no more in our land and our islands. Then came tall blond white men from the northeast who fought against us, but in between periods of fighting they intermarried with us until we became more like them and they more like us.

"But our men seldom went long without fighting against men of other districts."

For some time, the man in the hypnotic trance babbled on about fighting between clans and about periods of hunting in the hills. The medicine man decided not to ask too much of him on the first attempt. He spoke to the hypnotized man gently but firmly and told him that in future he would go back into his trance, instantly, at any time when the medicine man would say certain words to him. These words were carefully repeated by the medicine man, and the man in the trance was told to repeat them many times in order to drill them into his memory. He was told that whenever he heard those particular words he would fall asleep immediately and his subconscious mind would begin recalling the inherited memories stored in his brain.

He was told that when he became awake he would remember nothing of what he had said or what he had recalled while he was asleep. He was then told to become awake.

Sandy woke and sat up. It seemed to him that he had simply dropped off to sleep for a few seconds. He looked around and said to the medicine man, "So it didn't work, eh? I am now wider awake than when I sat down. For a few moments there, I thought you were going to put me to sleep. What went wrong? Was my skull too thick for your medicine to penetrate?" he asked with a smile.

"Quite the contrary," the medicine man answered solemnly. "You not only went to sleep but you talked sensibly, at length, and told me things that could not have come from your ordinary range of memories."

He then told Sandy what he (Sandy) had said while in the hypnotic trance.

Sandy was amazed at what he heard. The more he thought about it, the more he became interested in the magic powers of this "uncivilized" medicine man. He was interested in what he himself had mentioned while in the hypnotic trance.

He remembered, hazily, things he had read or had heard about Picts, Scots, Kelts, Romans, Danes, and Norwegian Vikings, and the reputed migration of the Dalriads from Ireland to Scotland after the arrival of the Romans in Britain. But from what land any of those people, other than the Romans, had come to Ireland, he did not know. He could remember references to Fingals or the blond Danes and to the Black Danes but he could not recall whether the Gaelic term for the Black Danes meant Danes from the eastern side of the north sea or the people he had been taught in school were the Danes, the people of Ancient Greece.

He spoke of this to the medicine man, who told him that in their next attempt to recall inherited memories they would try to find out something of the inherited memories going back before the ancestral arrival in Ireland and the subsequent move to the highlands and the islands of Scotland.

On the following evening the performance was repeated, but, while Sandy spoke much of happenings in the Island of Skoti or Ireland, and the movement northward to Scotland, no real progress was made in recalling memories of times before the arrival of Sandy's ancestors in Ireland.

After a day of meditation, the medicine man decided upon a different course of action. That evening, when the big white man went into the trance he was told not to talk but to think and to dream. He was told over and over again, by the medicine man, to try to recall things that had happened before his ancestors arrived in Ireland. He was told that for three nights he should do this, but that each morning as daylight came he would awake and would not remember anything he might have dreamed during the night. He would carry on his normal activities during the day. After three nights spent in the hypnotic trance, he would then be ready to take paper and pen in hand and write what would appear to him to be just thoughts from the inherited memories stored in his subconscious mind. He must write whatever thoughts came into his head without questioning the reason for his desiring to write those thoughts. He was told that the more he would write the more new thoughts would come into his head, because of the stimulated inherited memories in the storeroom of his brain.

On waking in the morning after his third night of hypnotic sleep, without talking while asleep, Sandy felt slightly dizzy and with a strange dull ache in his head. He told the medicine man about this.

"I was afraid of this," the medicine man admitted gravely, "but it is not serious. I have already prepared a brew to relieve such discomfort in your head. You have had three long nights of stimulated brain activity without normal sleep. Drink this and lie down. You will soon go into normal sleep. You should sleep as much as you can during this day and tonight. Tomorrow will be soon enough for you to begin writing."

"You will wish to write in your own language, and you should do so, but from time to time you should pause, and translate into our tongue what you have written, and dictate it to my daughter so that she may transcribe it in our system of writing in order that I may read it."

The elderly medicine man continued talking to Sandy. "So that you can write without too much interruption, for a few days, and because I have important matters to attend to at some distance from here, I will depart from this place tomorrow morning, early, and will be absent about half of one moon. During my absence you will, of course, live in my dwelling with my wife and our daughter, and my nephew who will provide food for the household and who will assist my daughter in nursing you back to health and back onto your feet."

The big white man did as the medicine man had told him to do. On the following morning, after a hearty breakfast, he began to write, in English.

Immediately dozens of scenes flashed into his mind, like normal memories of happenings in his past life, but these were more like daydreams or like imaginings of scenes he had never witnessed but had "thought up" during flights of fancy or daydreaming.

He could not decide what to write about first. As quickly as he tried to concentrate on one scene in his mind something else came into his mind's eye and he began chasing another idea. Then, suddenly, the idea popped into his head; why not begin somewhere, anywhere, and then follow whatever came into his mind from that starting point. He began to write:

I recall standing talking with several tall, reddish-haired, freckled-faced, men and women, all dressed in some strange garments and all talking in the NAY-HE-YA-WAYOO language—strange, but I seem to think of that name as NAY-HE-TLA-WAY-WIN; why the TL in the middle of it, I do not know—but there seemed to be TL sounds in some of the words which are slightly different from those of my vocabulary.

We were discussing the things we must do in order to repair the strange large man-made structure near us. I remember, now, we arrived in this country by means of this structure, seeking to find the descendants of some of our people who came to this country many many years before our time, and with whom we had maintained contact for some time, but eventually all contact was lost.

It was assumed that the original visitors from our distant world had been unable to survive or to reproduce their kind in this world. Explorers were sent to investigate and reported that some great changes had taken place, evidently caused by a great change in the axis of the earth. What had formerly been land was now all or partly under water and patches of new land had appeared—the latter, of course, being barren of vegetation. Tests also showed considerable change in the atmosphere making it unlikely that beings of our type could live long in it.

Then, ages later, by means of our own distant vision apparatus we were able to see that vegetation appeared to cover much of the barren land, and it was decided that a new investigation should be made, in the hope that there might be some descendants of the original colonists from our world. That was the purpose of our being there.

When we tested the atmosphere outside before we opened the door of our transporter structure we were prepared to find air that would be difficult, if not impossible, to breathe. But, to our surprise and pleasure, we found that we could breathe the air of this world, and we could move about on the land without any difficulty. We found evidence of widespread civilization along the banks of a number of great rivers and their tributaries.

We came to the surface of the earth near the junction of two great rivers; one flowing from the northwest, and one flowing from the northeast, with the larger river, below the confluence of the two, flowing toward the south.[9]

We found many intelligent people, but it was clearly evident that the ancient people from our world had intermarried with some other race or races. Although they spoke practically the same language that we did, the most of the people we found were different in general appearance from our people. Nearly all had black hair, brown or black eyes, and instead of the spotted or freckled skin of our people, these people had skin of the uniform pale copper color of the spots or freckles of our people.

It was just as if the freckles had spread all over their bodies and blotted out the whitish skin between the original freckles.

There were to be seen many buildings of wood, and structures of what looked like stone but we were told that most of such structures were made of sun-dried brick. Many of the buildings were on top of extensive structures of man-made hills of earth.

There were extensive fields of many kinds of cultivated vegetation in addition to very extensive tracts of forests. The people tilling the fields and living in the structures seemed to be highly intelligent and living in peace and plenty.

Things are coming into my head, now, in more orderly fashion and I think faster than I can write, so, because my writing will always be behind my thinking, I shall, in future, write in the past tense; at least, that is what I seem to think right now.

We had arrived safely. I am not trying to recall where we came from, but I could remember that something had gone wrong with our man-made structure that had enabled us to be transported to this world. Repairs had to be made before more men or material could be transported to us, or before we could be returned to our homeland. This meant that it would be necessary for our skilled people among us to find certain minerals and to use them in making repairs to our apparatus.

Strange as it seems to me, at this time, I realize now that I was one of the technical experts of our party, and my name was Kay-nook. Another of the technical experts was my own twin sister, May-koo-stik.

We talked with the wisest and most widely traveled men of the strangers among whom we were stranded. To them, we were magicians with powers and knowledge far beyond anything they possessed, but they were friendly and helpful. We were told that one of the minerals we were most anxious to obtain was known to exist near a large fresh water lake far to the north and west, in a land where the summer was very short and where the great river draining the lake flowed northward—not southward as did the stream where we were.

The most important mineral we sought was black and hard and heavy and brittle, with peculiar properties. The other was in metallic form, rather soft, yellow and very heavy. We knew it simply as "the yellow metal" but now I recognize it as what white men of today call 'gold.' We were told that this yellow metal could be found on the beaches of a certain part of the southern side of an island (or an island-like peninsula) in the great salt lake or ocean far to the east of where we were.

The decision of the leaders of our party, including my sister and myself, was that my sister would lead a party of native earth people to seek the black stony mineral in the far northwest, and I should lead a similar party to seek the yellow metal in the northeast.

Before we left home, my father, who was a great chief or government official as well as being a great scientist, gave me a small plate of yellow metal on which was inscribed the key to our written language. He instructed me to carry it at all times and to protect it from loss. If at any time I was to go on a dangerous mission I must leave the plate in the care of my twin sister, to whom similar instructions were given about wearing and taking care of it.

Because we were both starting out on what appeared to be equally dangerous but equally imperative missions, my sister and I decided to cut the yellow metal plate or talisman into two parts and each of us would carry one part. If necessary, each of us knew how to supply the inscriptions on the part we did not carry.

The plate was carefully cut in two, with a zigzag cut. We referred to the section carried by my sister as the "west half" and the section carried by me was referred to as the "east half." In referring to directions, we extended our left hand toward the place of the rising sun and our right hand toward the place of the setting sun. We would then be facing southward and midway between the places of the rising sun and the setting sun would be due south.

My sister was accompanied by one man and one woman of our people, they being man and wife, and by a large party of men and women of the black-haired people under the leadership of one of their chiefs. He was a fairly young man, a few years older than I, who was a very intelligent man highly skilled in all of the arts and sciences, such as they were, of the earth people. His sister went along as a companion for my sister. Several of the men who went with this party were much older than their leader. They were experienced travelers who would act as guides for the expedition.

Similarly, several of the men of my expedition were quite elderly, but there were many younger men who would do the heavy work involved in our travels over wild country. As we did not know how long we would be away, many of the men were accompanied by their wives, but all children were left behind. We worked our way upstream for many days; then across low mountains and down a stream running in a southerly direction into the salt sea where twice between each successive risings of the sun the water withdrew from the shoreline and twice in each such period the water rose and returned, being pushed and pulled by the moon. We thought this strange at the time but as I write this it seems very ordinary, and simply the ebb and flow of the tides.

After our arrival at the sea coast, we engaged local men accompanied by their wives to guide us in our journey along the coast. We worked our way northeastward and found that the range between high tide and low tide kept becoming greater and greater until it was several times the height of a tall man.[10]

At last we came to a large river, from the north, where the inrushing tidal waters, pinched between rock walls, rushed upstream so fast that they made a waterfall *into*[11] the river. From this point we struck southward to the island and followed around its western end and along its southern shore until we came to a place where the mighty waves of the ocean had washed away soft layers of rock, exposing narrow layers of hard white rock, which, in turn, were ground together by the lashing of the waves and from these layers of white hard rock came the small specks of dust of the yellow metal. These specks of the yellow metal, being heavy, accumulated in depressions or troughs in the rocks under the white sand.

Soon after we arrived at the place of the yellow[12] metal the storms of winter set in. Giant waves lashed the beaches where we had begun to extract the yellow metal from the sands. We were forced to establish a winter camp and to wait until the winter storms and cold weather had ended. When, at last, spring came, we began again to collect the yellow metal, but progress was slow and it was almost midsummer before we had accumulated the amount I considered necessary—this being approximately my own weight.

This may have been more than we needed but, having found it so difficult to gather, we decided to take at least that much back with us, rather than risk having to come again for more. While some men were gathering the heavy yellow sand and separating it from the much lighter white sand, others were hunting animals for tough skins in which to pack the yellow sand in quantities that could be carried easily and safely.

One day, while gathering the sand, we saw a very large and very strange appearing canoe go westward along the coast. It had a sail and was sailing with the wind. It disappeared behind a point and we thought no more about it, but, in the night, one of our men who was on watch saw men attempting to carry away some of our bags of yellow metal. There was a fight. More men attacked us and all our men took part in it. When daylight came we found that several of our men were dead or mortally wounded, but we had fared better than the attackers. All of them had been killed except two who lived for only two days after the attack.

One of the men with us, from the nation of the natives where we first came to the salt water on our journey eastward, was able to converse, after a fashion, with the men from the big canoe who had attacked us. We were told that occasionally such large canoes or ships crossed the ocean from some far away land to the southeast. These great canoes carried men seeking fish which were caught in large quantities and taken ashore and dried. When a great canoe became loaded with dried fish it would return to the southeast.

Whenever men from these great canoes had contact with the native people on the western side of the salt ocean they invariably asked questions about the location of a place where, in ages past, men from the eastern side of the ocean had found quantities of the yellow metal which they had taken to their homeland. Since then, many others had sought the location of the yellow metal but had never been able to find it. The fishermen always kept looking for it.

Our guide told us that his people had always refused to tell strangers where the yellow metal could be found, because their wise men for ages past had told them not to tell men from across the salt water where the gold could be found. These wise men had said that when the men from the far side of the ocean learned of the yellow metal they would come in swarms and would take for themselves not only the gold but all the land and would kill off all the people who lived on the western side of the salt water. He told us that we had been guided to the location of the gold only because we had come from the land; from the west, and because I carried the plate of yellow metal which they looked upon as some sort of sacred charm.

From the two dying men of the strangers who had attempted to rob us of our yellow metal, we learned that they and their companions had been fishing and were about to return to their homes with the great canoe loaded down with dried fish but a northeasterly wind had blown them in the wrong direction for two days and they had decided to find a sheltered harbor to wait until they had a favorable wind.

When they saw us digging in the sand they suspected we might be at the source of the yellow metal. They turned in to the bay, to the west of us and when the wind dropped at night, they paddled back to where we were.

We took possession of the great canoe with its load of dried fish. Our guide had seen enough of large canoes to know how to handle the sails and the long-handled paddles.

As the easterly winds continued to blow, we decided to use this great sailing canoe to carry some of us back to the western side of the salt water instead of retracing our roundabout route to the place of the yellow metal. There were too many persons in our party for all to travel on the captured sailing canoe. I did not wish to risk loss of the yellow metal by taking all of it with me, therefore, I entrusted about one third of it to one of my companions who had acted as my chief assistant. He was to return to our starting point by retracing the route we had followed to arrive at the place of the yellow metal. Even if by some mischance my portion of the metal should be lost, his portion should be ample to supply the immediate needs of our people at the space transporter.

Before we split into two parties, we decided that the acting chief of the other party should carry, as a token of his authority, a duplicate of the half of the golden talisman which I carried and which had so impressed local people, with whom we had had to deal along our route, with the importance of our mission. Our gold was in the form of dust so we made the duplicate from a piece of metal we found on the captured canoe. The metal was not gold but was brownish in color and slightly yellowish. The man to whom it was entrusted was fully aware of its significance and he was instructed to guard it carefully until it would be returned to me or to my sister.

We believed that if we sailed due westward we would arrive at the mainland north of the great hook of land jutting out into the salt water which we had passed as we journeyed northward along the coast.

Four days and four nights we sailed westward with the wind behind us. The sky high overhead was gradually becoming filled with smoky haze and the sun appeared only as a red ball in the sky. At night there was a strange glow in the western sky. On the evening of the fourth day we sighted land, far away but straight ahead of us. Soon after darkness came, the wind began to fall gradually and we made very slow progress. By about midnight we were in calm air and our great canoe was making no forward motion on the surface of the water. We were prepared to use our long paddles or oars to propel the great canoe toward land if the air was still calm when daylight came.

When daylight came, at last, we could see forested hills only a few miles away. Then, suddenly, the land seemed to disappear in a vast cloud of smoke that rolled toward us. It was as if the whole land mass had sunk into the sea. Rapidly, the great cloud of smoke or steam approached us, and then the wind began to blow from the land. The smoke was so dense we could hardly breathe and we were glad to sail with the wind in order to find air we could breathe.

In a very short time we were being blown directly away from the land, or from where we had last seen the land before it seemed to disappear into the sea. We hoped that if we would reach the island where we had spent the winter we might find relief from the smoke, as we believed that the island would not be in danger of being burned, if it was only forest fires that had produced the smoke.

We sailed much faster, with the wind from the west, than we did with the wind from the east. When four nights and four days had gone by since we reversed our direction, and we had not sighted land, we knew that we had been blown too far south to strike the island, or, perhaps the island itself had been swallowed by the sea.

There was too much smoke for us to see the sun, but there was enough light to distinguish day from night. After about ten days we found that we were in warmer water, and in air containing less smoke. We did not know where we were. The violent winds had died down and we began to see the sun enough to let us know that we were moving eastward and northward.

Since we knew that the fishermen from whom we had taken the ship had lived on the eastern side of the ocean, we believed that we would eventually come to land. Fortunately for us, there was food enough on the ship to keep our party of fifteen men and twelve women from starving, although eating dried, salt fish made us thirsty, and if it had not been for occasional showers of rain we would not have had enough fresh water to last us. We spread sails to catch the rain and this supplied the fresh water we needed.

One night as we were drifting fairly slowly towards the east we suddenly heard the sound of waves breaking on a shore and almost before we knew what was happening we were being carried by the wind and by a current of water or rising tide into an inlet in a rocky shore. Soon after we had entered the inlet our ship struck the rocks with a resounding crash and the ship began to fill with water. Two of the men on the front end of the ship must have been thrown overboard and were drowned in the darkness. We must have gone aground near high tide because when daylight came we were high and dry on a small rocky islet and in no danger of sinking.

Soon after daylight came, we noticed men approaching. They were in round-shaped boats like baskets made of small tree trunks lashed together and covered with animal skins of some kind. These men were armed with bows and arrows but made no threatening signs and seemed to be more curious than antagonistic. We made peaceful signs to them and one of the strange shaped basket boats came close to our wrecked ship. The men were smaller than our men and their hair was black but not as black as the men I had brought with me from the place where our space-transporter had landed. Their hair was finer in texture and there were various shades of brown and grey as well as black. The skin of these people was pinkish white and most of the people had blue or grey eyes.

We could not understand each other in our attempts at speaking but we were able to make signs that were more or less understand-able, and, of course, in time we learned enough of their language and they learned enough of ours so that communication was no longer any serious problem.

We found the natives to be friendly, and they invited us to live on their land in the understanding that we would join forces with them in protecting their territory from attack by unfriendly neighboring tribes. This we agreed to do.

When we first stepped ashore on this strange land, the natives were surprised to see us gather together with each man and woman holding both hands high above his or her head and standing with heads bowed toward the east and remaining silent for the time of three hundred heartbeats, as counted by our medicine man. The natives of this land, so new to us, did not know, at the time, that each man and woman of our party was offering a silent prayer to the Great Spirit for saving us from the horrors of the destruction of their homeland and the perils of the long voyage on the sea, and the miraculous escape from being blown onto a rock shore. All realized that only the Great Spirit could have guided the ship into that har-bor, because it was not by any skill on our part that we had avoided death by shipwreck on that rocky shore.

We could see no possibility of being able to return across the ocean and there was nothing for us to do but to live as best we could in this new green-clad land.

One of the two men who were drowned the night we arrived left a young widow. She became my wife and, in time, we were blessed with a family of children, two sons and three daughters.

Our older son had black hair like his mother, but the second son had red hair like his father, as did two of the daughters, particularly the younger of the two.

I remember trying to decide to which son I should intrust the half of the Golden Talisman that I carried. The dark-haired boy was the elder and, according to the customs of my native land he should become my heir, and to him should be given the Golden Talisman, but, on the other hand, he was in his physical appearance an alien to our race and I wondered if it would be right for me to leave the talisman with him when the younger son was so truly a member of my race in his physical appearance and mental characteristics.

Now, this comes to me as a modern afterthought of a man of the year 1725. Perhaps the talisman was given to one brother and I was descended from the other! or, more likely, from the youngest red-haired daughter. That might account for my having no other inherited memories of the Golden Talisman.

This is the end of the writing by Alexander MacDonald.

12
PAPEET'S RECALL OF INHERITED MEMORIES

Two days after Papeet had finished transcribing the story written by Sandy, her father and his party returned. Kesee Pay was very pleased to learn that Sandy's injuries were improving favorably and that the writing of Sandy's story was ready for him to read.

"We have had a long and rather tiresome journey, but everything went well with us. I am happy to be able to tell you that I have brought from its hiding place the unopened container of my grandfather's records which was safely hidden in a cave on the Sacred Hill. After I have had some rest and after I have studied carefully Papeet's transcription of your recollections from inherited memories we shall consider opening the container."

After a good night's rest, Kesee Pay began reading the story that Papeet had transcribed. In one or two places he paused to ask questions which Papeet or Sandy answered.

The medicine man was much excited by Sandy's story, although his solemn Indian face did not show it. "You have done well, my friend," he said. "You may think that much of what you have written is just a record of daydreams or idle imaginings, but I know better than you do what it all means. You have written from the inherited memories stored in your subconscious mind, memories of ancestor after ancestor, passed on from father to son, time after time, and the records of each one, from his own birth to the time he begat his successor, was added to the records he had inherited from his father, and all these records are carried by the last one to be born. I have said 'from father to son' but I could equally well have said 'from mother to daughter' because each carrier inherits memories from both father and mother. You do not know where the original "east half" of the Golden Talisman may be now because you have no inherited memories of it after it left the possession of your direct ancestor. It is possible that, in the course of time, you may have inherited some memories of it through crossbreeding with some descendant of a later possessor but such memories may be too faint for me to revive at this time. I shall not try now, to follow that possibility because I believe that you have indicated another more direct line of action to be followed."

"What might that be?" asked Sandy. "The only thing I can think of right now is that, since you are in possession of the actual "west half" of the talisman, you yourself may have inherited memories of its history back to where it was given to the twin sister of my ancestor Kaynook. But how can you be put into a trance to recall those memories? You can not put yourself into a controlled trance can you?"

"No, I can not do that but I am not the only one who has those inherited memories."

"Who else is there?" asked Sandy quickly. "I understood that your father is no longer living."

"Quite right. My father is dead, and so are my brothers, but my daughter is here and she must have memories that go back to the first of our ancestors who received this part of the talisman. I do not know how far back that may go; perhaps only a few generations or perhaps many centuries, or perhaps even back to that red-haired twin sister of Kaynook."

"That's it," an excited Sandy almost shouted, "that would account for the strange feeling both Papeet and I had when we first met—that we had known each other somewhere before. Like in the old rhyme, 'As often on some crowded street some half remembered face I meet, methinks I've seen that face before albeit it on some far off shore, or distant planet where we dwelt of yore.' "

Papeet, who had been listening to her father and Sandy, showed her excitement in this interesting development. "You must surely let me try, my father. Perhaps my hair inherited memories to grow red and wavy just as Sandy's did. Don't you think we should try to find out if you and I are direct descendants of Kaynook's sister? I would very much like to help in trying to find out.

"The Great Spirit must have some purpose in bringing us together and I think it would not be right for us to stop until we have investigated everything we can think of that might help us to solve the mystery of the Golden Talisman and the purpose behind the bringing together of the two parts of the talisman at this time."

"You are a wise young woman, my daughter," admitted the medicine man proudly. Then, turning to Sandy, he said, "I have changed my mind about something. When I arrived here today I intended to tell you of my intention to open the container immediately and to read some of the records in it, but now I think it would be far better for Papeet and for all of us if we try to recall some of her inherited memories before we look at any of my grandfather's records. Let us eat and rest today, and tomorrow we will try to learn something from Papeet's memories."

On the following morning, Kesee Pay began his attempt to have inherited memories in the mind of his daughter recalled. He had no difficulty in putting her into the hypnotic trance, using the same procedure that he had followed with Sandy. For a while, he talked with her and asked questions which she answered clearly and logically. He repeatedly asked her to try to think back into the past and to try to recall how the Golden Talisman came to the country where they now were.

Sandy was ready with writing material to record anything Papeet might say. He wrote down her father's instructions and questions addressed to her, and her replies.

After some preliminary questions and answers, Papeet began a narrative:

"I remember waiting in my dwelling, a building of logs covered with bark, for my husband who had gone southward with a party of men to explore land where our people used to live before the great fire disaster destroyed all vegetable and animal life on it. For generations the land had been barren and uninhabitable. We seemed to know that long ago it was a wonderful land with fertile soil where thousands upon thousands of people lived happily. For generations we had been living to the north of the devastated land, in the long east and west strip of forest country that had escaped the destruction of our former homeland, but where we were forced to live was cold in winter and swarming with flies in the short summer. We could not cultivate the soil to any extent, so we lived mostly on the flesh of animals, birds and fish. The vegetation of the forests was gradually extending southward along the northern border of the devastated area but many of our people were filled with fear of another catastrophe and they resisted the pleas of some of our leaders to make an attempt to return to the land of our forefathers at the fork of two great rivers, south of the great lakes.

"My husband was one of the men trying to lead the people back to the land where tradition said our people used to live in peace and plenty before the great and terrible catastrophe that killed all but a few who were away from home on an expedition of some sort to the land of ice and snow in the far north. I remember looking at the gold plate with the strange lines marked on it, but I had no idea of any meaning those lines might have. The plate or talisman had been given to me by my father who had received it from his father. Because my only brother was no longer alive, my father gave it to me. He instructed me to give it to my son when he became a man. I remember, now, that I gave it to him.

"I remember that my husband returned from the south and told us that he had visited the land of our ancestors and found that vegetation had returned to cover much of the land but that strange people from the south had come up the great river and had taken possession of much of the land and were cultivating it. They were growing and harvesting crops of things they used for food instead of having to depend on meat, fish, wild rice and a few roots such as we had to depend on for our food.

"He reported that the strange people who had taken over our ancient homeland had reconstructed wooden buildings on some of the large earthworks that the ancient people had built long before the great disaster. When my husband and others talked by sign language with these intruders of our ancient country and tried to tell them that we owned the land they had reoccupied in our absence, the strangers laughed at them, at first, and told them that it was *their* land now and they intended to keep it. In the end, my husband's party was surrounded and told to go back north into the forests and to stay there. They were unmistakably informed that if any more of our people were seen in the country they would be killed.

"My husband wanted to collect a large number of men to form an army that could go south and take back the land from those intruders from the south."

After pausing for a few moments, Papeet resumed her narrative. "Now, I seem to be some other person traveling with an army of men. I am not a woman but am a man. I am thinking about my grandfather who led the party back to our old homeland but was forced to return home. He was disappointed that his people would make no further attempt to reoccupy their old homeland in the

97

warmer country to the south, but here am I, leading the army that my grandfather had hoped to lead. I am wearing the Gold Talisman attached to a belt around my waist. Now, we are approaching a large village or town in the land where there are wooden buildings on the tops of strange man-made hills or mounds of earth surrounded by cultivated fields. We are slowly moving southward but meeting much resistance from the inhabitants who are facing us from behind earthworks. Many men are being killed on both sides but we are gradually regaining control of the land." There was another pause. Then Papeet continued:

"Again, I seem to be some other person. I seem to recall that our people had been living for many generations on the land we took back from the intruders from the south, but I also remember that our long sojourn in the forested land of the north had caused many of our people to prefer the life of the hunter to the life of the tiller of the soil and much of the cultivated land we repossessed was allowed to become covered with wild vegetation. The land of our ancestors, which had provided living room and food stuff for tens of thousands of persons before the great disaster, and which, before we repossessed it, had supported hundreds of people of some southern race for the relatively few generations of their occupation of it, was now gradually but steadily going back to wild land again with only villages here and there where the land was cultivated, and the buildings on the tops of the old man-made structures of earth were allowed to rot and to become overgrown with trees, vines and bushes.

"Again, I seem to be another person, this time we are on the move again back to the forests of the north that had been our home for so many generations. Two things had helped to drive us back to the north. Strangers from the south had made attempts to take our land from us. They kept intruding more and more into our hunting grounds and when they and our people met there was war, and much killing.

"One summer, the season began with terrible storms; there were terrific winds and gigantic black and white clouds, and much thunder and lightening. At the time of the longest days there were many strange clouds in the sky with whirling black tails that looked like beaver tails hanging out of black clouds. These tails sucked up into the sky grass, sticks, tents and even trees. Wherever these cloud-tails passed they left trails of twisted and uprooted trees. Then, soon after midsummer, the sun and the moon became red and the sky became darkened, not with clouds but as if with a high, solid sky full of smoke. With only dim sunlight the air became colder and colder long before the proper autumn season.

"But before the sky became so full of smoke, one of our southern villages had been attacked by enemy forces and we had taken a number as captives, intending to hold them as slaves, but in a few days they all became suddenly ill, and died, one after another. Then our people were stricken with the same illness and so many died that within a few moons eight out of every ten of our people had died. Those who recovered from the illness became convinced that the illness was something that was left over from the great catastrophe of the past and had been stirred up into the air by the beavertail clouds that lifted into the air the soil from the cultivated fields.

"These people became determined to migrate to the north away from the old land that they believed to be cursed.

"Some of our people went to the northeast, crossing the rivers between the lakes. Some went north to the northern shores of the great lakes and stayed in the forested areas on the northern and eastern sides of the lakes, but some of us went to the western end of the largest lake of all, the one we know as Kitshe Kumee. Then we moved inland to the edge of the treeless flat country that extends toward the home of the setting sun for as far as the eye can see, even after days of walking toward the sunset. With the many animals living on the open plains or in the forests we were always sure of food. It all seems to be hazy now, as if I had been dreaming and am now half awake. I can not remember anything more."

The medicine man spoke to her gently and told her not to talk but to rest a while.

He sat in meditation while Sandy silently read over some of the notes he had written. After a while, the medicine man spoke softly to his daughter and told her to become awake and in her normal condition, which she did.

Papeet was amazed when her father and Sandy told her of some of the things she had said while in the trance.

"Why do I not remember any of this now that I am awake?" she asked her father.

"That is something I can not answer," admitted her father rather sadly. "The Great Spirit allows some of us to make use of certain powers that are beyond our powers of intelligence to understand. It is probable that it is that very lack of intelligence to understand that prevents our being told the reasons why many things are as they are; just as sharp knives must be kept away from the hands of a child until the child has the intelligence to know how to handle knives properly."

"Were you satisfied, my father, with the results of your experiment?" inquired Papeet.

"I had hoped that you might recall happenings in the past, back to where you first received the west half of the Golden Talisman, but we seem to have reached only part of the way back to that time. I am wondering if another attempt would produce any earlier recollections. Your memories seemed to jump back and forth in time."

Sandy, who had been thinking seriously now spoke up, saying, "I think it would be best to do something like what you did with me. Why not let Papeet rest the remainder of the day while I read to her all the things she told us. Then after a good night's sleep she could be put into the trance condition tomorrow and you could give her instructions to try to recall everything possible with respect to the time when she first came into possession of the section of the Golden Talisman. I believe it would be best if she did not talk while in the trance, but when she awakes she is to remember all the things that came to her mind from those mysterious stores of memories. When she becomes awake, she could either write what she remembers, as I did, or she could tell me and I could record it."

"Yes," agreed the medicine man. "I believe that is the procedure we should follow."

Later in the day, after Sandy had rewritten and filled in from memory a few gaps in the dictation from Papeet that he had recorded, he read the whole thing to her. She sat with her eyes closed but listening intently. Several times she held up her hand to stop him. The third time this happened, she told him: "Just there something flashed into my mind that must have been a scene that I recalled from the past, but it came and went so quickly that I could not concentrate on any particular item in the picture; but it was like a scene I can recall by thinking about some actual happening in the past. But when I try to recall some actual happening in my own life I can hold the scene, or group of scenes, although they may be blurry or overlapping, but, with these scenes recalled from other lives, they are only flashes of very short duration and not connected with each other. I wish I could see them longer or remember them better. Of course, I do not know whether those flashes are memories of actual scenes or whether they are simply the work of my imagination and have no real relation with actual scenes in the lives of anybody."

On the following day, the medicine man gave careful instructions to his daughter after she lay back in her hypnotic sleep. He told her to try to concentrate on things that had happened earlier than the time she had described in her trance on the day before. He told her not to hurry but take all the time she needed and that when she was ready to come out of the trance she should do so of her own will without his having to wake her; but if he decided that it was better for him to wake her, he would do so and she must then come back to normal out of the trance whenever he said "wake up" to her three times in quick succession.

For several hours Papeet slept, apparently in normal sleep, but after a time Sandy became a little worried, thinking she might be sleeping too long. He urged her father to wake her, but the older man shook his head and said, "Let us wait a little longer."

Half an hour went by and Sandy was just about to ask the medicine man to bring his daughter out of her trance when she suddenly sat up, rubbed her eyes, and looked around. Almost instantly she was wide awake and full of excitement as if she had just had a wonderful happy dream and wished to tell about it to everybody.

"Oh, my father!" she cried. "I have had the most wonderful experience. I did not have to do any thinking or trying to recall scenes from the past. The dream spirit woman, Powakun Iskwayo, came to me and told me all about the things you wanted to know. She talked to me for a long time. Then she told me to go asleep for a while and then she came back and talked to me some more. Have I been asleep more than a day and a night?"

"No," said her father. "It seemed almost like that to us sitting here waiting and watching you; but you were asleep only a few hours."

"But I could not have heard and seen all the things I did in only a few hours," protested the girl.

"You saw things?" interrupted Sandy.

101

"Yes, indeed," replied the girl. "The dream spirit told me to look at a crystal she held in her hand. As she talked to me, I seemed to see right through the crystal and could see things life size. As she talked to me the scenes changed constantly and it was just as if I were seeing the actual things she was talking about. I will tell you the things I was told, but, Sandy, you will never to able to write as fast as I will talk, so just take some notes on points about which you wish to ask me later and listen to my story. I am sure I will be able to remember enough so that we can fill in the whole story later."

13
MAY-KOO-STIK

Papeet began her story: This is the story of May-koo-stik, twin sister of Kaynook, as told to Papee-tsha-koos, daughter of Kese-pay-pimoo-tay-oo, by her female dream spirit guardian:

May-koo-stik was very sad to leave her brother and her many friends but she realized that almost certainly the lives of all their party depended upon the success of her mission to find and bring back the heavy black mineral needed by the group at the great "space transporter." She was the one person in the party with the most expert knowledge of the rare mineral needed so urgently—just as her brother Kaynook was their expert on the heavy yellow metal.

Guided by the most experienced travelers of the local Nay-he-ya-way-oo people, her party worked its way up the great river flowing from the north. Their destination was the eastern end of a great lake in the far north country, hundreds of miles away. The expedition was made up of over fifty men and twenty women. All except three persons were members of the Nay-he-ya-way-oo Nation—the earth people who lived in the valley of the two great rivers and in the country between the two rivers and the five great lakes to the north of the fork of the two rivers. These people had lived there so long that they barely remembered the tradition that claimed they had originally lived far to the south and west, before the land they lived on had been destroyed by a great convulsion of nature set off by misguided men playing with powers they did not know how to control.

The leader of this expedition was, of course, the red-haired woman know as May-koo-stik. She was accompanied by a man and a woman of her own race, who were to act as her personal servants. They were husband and wife, the husband being named Muskwa and his wife being named Atikoos. The man in command of the Nay-he-ya-way-oo people was a chief named Okima. He was only about five years older than May-koo-stik. He was tall and well built, with straight jet black hair and dark brown eyes. He was accompanied by his young wife, whose name was Tanis, and by his sister Wapoosis. The latter had been chosen by May-koo-stik to go with them because she wished to have Wapoosis as her companion on the expedition, which was expected to take a full year or more— one summer season to reach their destination, one winter season and part of a warmer season to procure the mineral, and the remaining part of the summer season to return to their starting point.

It had been considered necessary to take a large party in order that there would be sufficient hunters to keep the expedition supplied with meat, and sufficient men to paddle, pole and portage the canoes in which they would have to travel.

Okima had traveled over part of the route but not all of it. Only five old men of the expedition had ever been near the lake where the ore was known to exist.

The days had already begun to shorten when the expedition started out, and for the first moon and nearly a half of another moon it was all upstream work, but all went well. Then they portaged across country to a river running northward and they drifted down this muddy red river to a large lake that stretched far to the northward but not quite in the direction they wished to travel. They left it to go up a river which flowed into the western side of the lake. They followed this river westerly for half a moon and then after another portage they came to a large river that flowed toward the north. On this stream, known locally as the Atlapaska, the current enabled them to cover greater distances each day and they arrived at their destination[13] less than half a moon before the cold weather began to make ice in the small lakes.

It was, of course, too late in the season to return to the south, so the first work was to establish a winter camp, in a sheltered valley where there were trees to provide wood for shelters and for fuel. During the longer winter, the men of the expedition who were not busy hunting to supply food for the camp mined the black ore and reduced it to powder. The black, hard and heavy material they sought was firmly embedded in hard rock. The mining and reduction of the rock to powder was slow and laborious work. A place had to be found where the ore veins were exposed. Only small amounts of the rock in its natural state could be broken off by hammering with hard rocks. Then fires would be made to heat the rock as much as possible. While the rock was at its hottest, water would be thrown on it to make the rock snap, crackle and become soft enough that some of it could be ground to powder by pounding it with rock hammers.

In some cases, holes were bored into the hard rock. This was a very slow process but worked surprisingly well. The holes had to be directed downward. A small straight rod of wood, with a disk of rock near the lower end to act as a flywheel, was held in position by one man while two other men made it twirl rapidly, first in one direction and then in the other direction. They caused this whirling motion by using a long bow with the bowstring looped around the rod so that when the horizontally held bow was pulled or pushed back and forth the string made the rod revolve. The bottom end of the rod was frayed just a little in order to hold dust of finely powdered white quartz rock. The lower end of the rod was always kept wet and well supplied with powdered quartz. The quartz being harder than the rock in which the veins of the black mineral occurred soon wore away the rock under the end of the rod; and by scooping out the powdered rock, from time to time, quite deep holes could be drilled in the rock.

After a line of these holes, not over a finger length apart, was drilled in the rock, the holes were hammered full of very dry wood. Then water was poured on the wood of all the holes at the same time. As the wood became wet it swelled. The swelling wood in the row of holes caused the rock to break all along the line of holes. In this way, large masses of rock could be obtained or split into smaller masses. The smaller masses could be heated almost white hot in fires and then suddenly quenched in water, or cooled rapidly by water poured on them. When this was done the nature of the rock became changed and was easily hammered into powder.

As the black mineral was much heavier than its surrounding rock, it was relatively easy to separate the heavy material from the lighter rock powder by flowing water over it, on a slightly sloping surface, and washing away the light rock powder.

The powdered black material was packed in tough moose hide bags; small bags that could easily be carried in the canoes and over portages. By the time when the days and nights were of equal length the members of the expedition had collected a total weight of black mineral equal to ten times the weight of Okima.

When the expedition established its winter camp there were no native people living in the vicinity, but there appeared evidence that people had been there at some time in the distant past and had carried on mining operations. In some places it was difficult to determine whether the apparent excavations were the work of man long ago or the work of nature in that land of extreme cold where water seeping into cavities in the rock would be frozen into solid ice with resulting swelling that often would shatter the rock. There was much discussion about whether the expansion of frozen water could have caused some of the peculiar features they found, but the question was settled unexpectedly only about four moons after the expedition arrived.

One bright, calm moonlit night they were surprised to hear dogs barking and men shouting. Soon they saw black objects approaching from the northwest and, in a few minutes they could see three teams of dogs dragging toboggans, with several men running behind each toboggan. When the dog drivers saw the camp and the members of the expedition they stopped in surprise. After a few minutes one man came forward toward the camp holding both hands high above his head to show that he had no weapons in them. He was allowed to come to within speaking distance of the people of the expedition. He spoke to them in a language which no member of the expedition could understand. He could not understand any of the questions put to him, but he indicated by signs that he wished to call one man from his party. Okima acted as spokesman for his companions and made signs to the stranger that one other man could come forward. It was found that this other man could speak enough of the Nayheyawayoo language to be understood without much difficulty. When it was assured that their intentions were peaceful, the dog drivers were welcomed at the camp and were given food— meat for themselves and fish for their dogs.

The strangers with the dogs remained in camp for several days but then departed and were seen no more. But while they were in camp, May-koo-stik and Okima questioned them about their knowledge of any earlier seekers of the black mineral. They were surprised to learn that the strangers firmly believed that many

many years earlier there had been a race of people who "came down from the sky" and lived for untold generations in a country far to the southwestward of the place where the black mineral was located and separated from this land by vile tasting water that humans could not drink.[14]

According to the information given by the strangers, the strange race of people was quite different from their own; in physical appearance and in their way of life. They had many magical things and had many magical powers that enabled them to do things that the black-haired people—the dog-drivers' ancestors—could not do. The interpreter for the "dog-drivers," as the strangers were called by May-koo-stik's party, pointed at her and at Muskwa and Atikoos and said:

"The stories handed down to us by our forefathers said that the ancient people from the sky were like you in appearance, with long, wavy, red hair and freckled faces, but we have never before seen people who looked like that and we came to believe that the stories of red-haired people were myths, like stories about giants, tiny dwarfs and fairies. But now that we have seen you we do not know how much to believe about any of those things we thought were myths."

The story, as pieced together by May-koo-stik and Okima, and others, was to the effect that the straight-black-haired people, the ancestors of the dog-drivers, had lived somewhere far, far away in a land where there was little or no snow but much heat, and many kinds of fruit growing on trees and vines. For some unknown reason, they slowly moved toward the northwest, from their earliest known place of habitation. In time, they came to the southeastern corner of the country where lived the red-haired people with the strange magical appliances and powers. For a time, the two races lived at peace with one another, but in the end friction developed into almost constant border warfare, although not on any large scale.

The red-haired people had access to the vile water ocean and on it they operated large ships that sailed to the land far on the eastern side of the ocean, and to parts of that land where there was no winter—just continuous summer where day and night were almost always of the same length of time.

Many times these ships brought back heavy loads of bags contain-

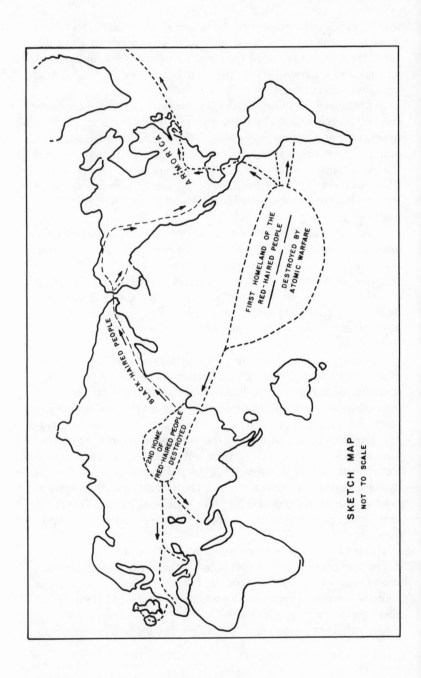

ARMORICA

FIRST HOMELAND OF THE
RED-HAIRED PEOPLE

DESTROYED BY
ATOMIC WARFARE

BLACK-HAIRED PEOPLE

2ND HOME
OF
RED-HAIRED PEOPLE
DESTROYED

SKETCH MAP
NOT TO SCALE

ing heavy black powder which the red-haired people used in their magic things that shot something like stars into the sky—stars that left long trails of smoke behind them. A large stock of the black powder was accumulated and strange substances were made from it in peculiar shaped buildings. One day while the red-haired magicians were shooting these stars into the sky, one suddenly turned back at full speed, right straight at the strange building. When it hit the building there was a terrific explosion. This had been witnessed by a few people on a mountain far away from the actual explosion. All the people within five days' walking distance of the site of the strange building had been killed and the country was laid waste over a very large area and remained forever desert land, or so the black-haired people believed.

Much of their race was destroyed by the explosion, fires, earthquakes and strange sicknesses which followed. The red-haired survivors were reported to have moved to the westward, but the survivors of the black-haired race worked their way back to the eastward, to the sea coast, but, over the centuries, they were driven northeastward by hostile races who had taken over their original homeland. They were gradually driven into the land of long cold winters, but they were spurred on by stories that some of their people had been carried as slaves on ships of the red-haired magicians to a warm land on the great island to the east of where their ancestors had lived. The black-haired people were unable to build or to operate the type of ships which had been used by the red-haired race.

The modern race of the dog-drivers[15] did not know how much of all this was myth or how much of it might be partly true. They knew only that the remnants of their race had slowly worked their way to the extreme eastern end of the land where they had lived. There they met members of a race of straight, black-haired people, somewhat smaller in stature than themselves, who traveled in skin boats in summer, and by means of sleds, hauled by dogs, in the winter, and who lived on fish and animals of the sea that, in turn, lived on fish. These fish-eating people[16] taught them how to travel by skin boats and by dog teams. They also told them about the great land to the east, on the other side of the vile tasting water, where there was a great river that flowed into the icy sea coming from such a great distance south that it sometimes carried large trees that could have grown only in a much warmer country than any land know to the fish-eating people.

After a time, the black-haired people from the south decided to try to cross the water to the land they had been told about. They longed for a warmer climate and hoped to find it by moving southward after they arrived in the land on the eastern side of the vile tasting water.

After they crossed the water to the new land they split into two groups. One group decided to attempt to work their way southward by following the shore. The other party thought it would be too dangerous to try to do this and they decided to work their way along the open water between the northern shore of the new land and the edge of the ice fields that stretched far to the north. The fish-eaters had told them of the great river that flowed from the south and often carried driftwood of large trees that they believed could only have grown in a much warmer climate.

The dog-drivers were descendants of the people who thus worked their way eastward to the great river and then southward upstream against the current of the river. Their intentions were to keep on moving southward but they had become aclimatized to the cold.[17]

During the winter, Okima's men had constructed additional canoes to carry the black powder and to lighten the loads of the other canoes, because they realized that working upstream against the current of the Atlapaska River would be a much more difficult job than drifting downstream with the current.

At last the pilgrimage back to the south began. At times the canoes could be paddled or poled, but in many long stretches of the river it was necessary for each canoe to be towed by men walking slowly along the water's edge with a long rope of rawhide attached to the canoe, not at the front end or bow but several foot lengths back from the bow. At the shore end of the rope were the men. Sometimes there were short rapids where the men on the shore would have to stand still while the steersman in the canoe pointed it out into the stream to let the force of the water on the side of the canoe force the latter to move away from the shore, but being attached by the long line to the shore, the water also forced the canoe upstream. Once the canoe was above the rapid water the men would walk along the shore and the steersman would keep it out in the stream until it was well clear of rapid water. At other times, the canoes had to be unloaded and everything had to be carried around the sections of rapid water.

At last, the expedition arrived at the place where they expected to cross over from the waters running toward the north, to the stream where the waters ran toward the south and the east. At this point, they were met by natives with the surprising news that about half a moon earlier there had been a terrific earthquake, or so it seemed to them, and this had been followed by terrible forest fires and fires in the grass of the open prairies—fires that burned deep into the ground. The natives said that the fires were worse in the southeast but were steadily advancing *against* the prevailing northwest winds. They claimed that many people had fled northward and westward to escape the onrushing flames.

May-koo-stik and her expedition reached the long river flowing easterly into the long north and south lake but, as they were still a very long distance from the lake, they decided to wait a few days or perhaps a few weeks until the danger from the fires would be over. They established a camp on the northern side of the river where they hoped they would be safe if the fire did not reach the northern bank of the river. They hoped that the river would serve as a fire-break to prevent the fire from burning the forests on the northern side of the stream.

While they waited, more and more people arrived from the southeast with unbelievable stories of destruction caused by fire and by some mysterious outbreak of unseen forces that caused death to humans, to animals and to vegetation of all kinds. The refugee people believed that all life on the land to the southeast had been destroyed except themselves and that they were the only survivors.

All members of the expedition were anxious to learn the fate of the people they had left behind near the junction of the two great rivers, far to the southeast of where they now found themselves. They all wanted to return home, particularly the young men; but wiser counsel of the older men prevailed, and it was decided to establish a more or less semi-permanent camp on the northern bank of the easterly flowing river which was known to the natives as the Kisiskatshewan River.

May-koo-stik and Okima and the older men of the expedition, after much discussion with the natives and with each other, decided it would be foolhardy for them to attempt to pass through the burnt

111

or destroyed area to reach their starting point without knowing how extensive the destroyed area might be. They hoped that the autumn rains and winter snow would put out the fires and wash away some of the evil effects of whatever had happened. Accordingly, preparations were made for another winter camp.

All went well for a time, but, after a great storm blew from the southeast for four days, the air became filled with smoke and dust that made breathing difficult until the rain came and cleared the air. Many of the people became ill with some strange malady that no local medicine man could identify or cure. In the course of less than one moon many people died. One of the first to die was Atikoos, the red-haired wife of Muskwa, and the personal attendant of May-koo-stik. Soon after that, Tanis, the wife of Okima, died, as did five of the older men of Okima's group of advisers.

Spring came at last and scouts were sent out by Okima. All brought back the same story—everything south of the Kisiskatshewan River was barren of life of all kinds; no vegetation, no animal life and even the waters of the lakes were poisoned and the shores piled up with the remains of dead fish. There seemed nothing for May-koo-stik and her expedition to do but to stay where they were and try to live as best they could.

There were many animals in the forests on the north of the Kisiskatshewan River and the members of the expedition who survived the strange sickness were able to find plenty of food during the winter. All had been looking forward to spring when they had hoped to resume their journey back to their old homeland in the south. All of them, especially May-koo-stik and Muskwa, hoped that they never again would have to experience the bitter cold of that long northern winter.

In the early summer, scouts were sent down the river to investigate the effects of the great fires, if any, on the northern side of the river. They went downstream to where the river entered the great north and south lake. They found little or no destruction of forests on the northern side of the river and they reported that animals and birds were plentiful there.

After much deliberation it was decided that no further attempts would be made to return to the south because it was evident that their homeland must have been destroyed.

Okima and the older men split the members of the expedition

into groups and assigned to them various hunting grounds so that no one group would be too large for the supply of game animals in each area.

Wapoosis, sister of Okima, who had been the constant and faithful companion of May-koo-stik, had fallen in love with red-haired Muskwa after his wife had died from the strange sickness that had also taken the life of the wife of Okima. Wapoosis asked May-koo-stik to allow her to be married to Muskwa, even if she was not of the red-haired race. At first, May-koo-stik hesitated because she hoped that they would all return to the people they had left behind with the "space transporter," but by the end of the second summer she gave up all hope of ever seeing her own people again and she gave her permission for Muskwa to marry Wapoosis.

In the discussions with Okima on this matter, May-koo-stik could not fail to see that Okima was becoming increasingly in love with her, herself, but because he looked upon her as almost a goddess from the sky he did not dare to mention this to her. Once it was decided that Muskwa and Wapoosis were to be married May-koo-stik proposed to Okima that they, too, should become man and wife. One of the older men of the party was an official medicine man and he supervised and led the tribal ceremonies in a double wedding.

As the years rolled by, Okima and May-koo-stik were blessed with children, as were all the married couples of the original expedition, and those couples formed when men of the expedition married women of the native people.

After many happy years together, May-koo-stik and Okima died and their oldest son became the possessor of the Golden Talisman. He, in turn, was succeeded by his son, and for generation after generation the talisman was passed on from father to son.

After many generations on the Kisiskatshewan River the descendants of May-koo-stik's expedition gradually extended their territory down the stream draining the great lake of dirty water into the salt water sea. Gradually they occupied land along the southern shore of the salt water and spread into the land to the east and to the south of the salt water. By this time, the country to the south was again becoming covered with vegetation, and, as the forest growth increased, the animals and birds from the north spread into it, so that, in time, there was life to support the human beings who dared risk their lives by extending their hunting grounds and living space toward the land that once was the homeland of their almost forgotten ancestors. In some cases, the Nayheyawayoo-speaking people met people from the south who also were extending their living space into the reforested land that had been made barren long, long ago by the great catastrophe.

Some of these people spoke mutually understandable dialects, but some of the tribes encountered spoke quite different languages and, in time, contact with these different tribes or groups of people resulted in many changes in the language, so that now the old Nayheyawayoo language has been altered into several dialects spoken by people whose living space extends from the headwaters of the Kisiskatshewan River to the great salt inland sea, and south across the river draining the great lakes, and still further southward and eastward to the great salt water ocean.

The official Keeper of the Golden Talisman and his branch of the people from the Kisiskatshewan River did not go to the salt water inland sea but lived for many generations in the Kisiskatshewan Valley and then gradually spread into the reforested country on the eastern side of the long north and south lake into which flowed the waters of the Kisiskatshewan River.

In due course, one of the direct descendants of May-koo-stik and her husband Okima became the official Keeper of the Golden Talisman. His name was Moosoom and he was the grandfather of Peyowah-mit, who was the grandfather of Kese-pay-pimoo-tay-oo, the father of Papee-tsha-koos.

Now this is the end of the story of May-koo-stik, and of her descendants who were Keepers of the Golden Talisman which she received from her twin brother Kaynook in the days before the great disaster that destroyed the homeland of the Nayheyawayoo people and that wiped out the great space transporter and the red-haired strangers who came with it from the sky.

14
PAPEET AND SANDY IN LOVE

Sandy and Papeet reread and checked carefully the manuscript before Papeet read it to her father. Her father listened to every word, and after she had finished he sat in meditation for what seemed to Sandy to be at least half an hour before he spoke a word. Then he said: "Thank you, my daughter, you have had a wonderful experience and you have reported it well. I am proud of you. You are a worthy daughter of our no longer mythical ancestress May-koo-stik of the wavy red hair and the more-than-mortal intelligence who came from some unknown part of the sky to this world in which we live, and from whom you have inherited not only your beautiful hair but your outstanding intelligence, wisdom, and good common sense."

Then, turning to Sandy he said: "After considering carefully all the information recalled from the inherited memories of Papeet and yourself, I have decided that I should, indeed, open the container holding the writings of my grandfather, Peyo-way-mit. I believe that the three of us should study them together and be guided by what may be revealed to us. I am now confident that, whether we do or do not have the two halves of the talisman, within the meaning of the instructions passed to me by my grandfather, we do have here the direct descendants of the twins from the sky who were the original possessors of the two halves of the original talisman, and the two halves of the talisman can be joined together exactly, even if one half is only a copy of the original; so, let us inspect the books that my grandfather wrote."

Without much difficulty, the container was broken open and eight books written in syllabic symbols were found to be in good condition despite the number of years since they had been carefully wrapped, packed, and sealed in an airtight container disguised as a small boulder of rock.

Two were copies of the books already in Kesee Pay's possession. He examined all the books to see if they had been damaged but did not attempt to read them. He said to his daughter "Sandy has had so many things to think about since you read to him 'The Eighth Book of Peyo-wah-mit' that it might be best if we begin by reading again that book."

Papeet and Sandy both agreed that this was a sound idea, and again Papeet read aloud the "Eighth Book" of her great grandfather.

While Papeet was reading aloud the "Eighth Book of Peyo-wah-mit," Sandy requested her several times to pause, and he asked her and her father to explain the meanings of certain expressions which were unfamiliar to him. Although his knowledge of the Indian language was extensive, Sandy was often hearing combinations of idea symbols in sequences that were new to him, and, whenever possible, he tried to obtain promptly the correct meaning and to have the expression registered correctly in his remarkable memory.

Sandy, Kesee Pay and Papeet had a general discussion on what had been written by Peyo-wah-mit. Sandy and Papeet were eager to begin the reading of another of the books, but Kesee Pay said that he wished to spend the remainder of the day thinking over the contents of the book in the light of recent developments. He said that after a night of meditation and sleep he would be ready to begin reading another book in the morning. Sandy and Papeet went outside to let him meditate undisturbed.

When they left the door of the dwelling of her father, Papeet helped Sandy to hobble to a fallen tree far enough away from the door that their voices would not disturb the older man. The shadows of the trees were lengthening but the air was not too cold for comfort as they sat side by side on the tree trunk.

Both were excited by the strange things revealed to them in the past few days, but there was another kind of excitement that each was trying to hide from the other. For a while, Sandy tried in vain to talk about other things but, finally, had to let Papeet know what was uppermost in his mind.

He said abruptly: "Papeet, I love you. I love you but I do not know what we can do about it. You may not want my love but before you say a word I want you to listen while I tell you about myself and the quandary I am in.

"You and I are members of what the modern world calls two

116

different races, but you and I know that we are both descended from not only the same race but from two persons who were, themselves, twin brother and sister; and, from that point of view, there is no reason in this wide world why we should not be married and have children. There is nothing in this world that I would rather have than to have you as *my* wife and the mother of *our* children."

Papeet remained silent but tears of emotion were gleaming in her eyes as Sandy continued:

"But there are other things that must be considered. Much as I love you, I could not take you away from your father, at this time, even if I had a place to take you to. On the other hand, I can not simply cast the white man's world aside and try to become a member of your people, great as the temptation might be, because I am under contract agreement with my employers, either to work with them under a renewed contract, if they so desire me to do, or to return next summer to the distant land across the sea from whence I came. I want you to be my wife some day but I can not honorably ask you to marry me until I know what kind of home life I can offer you.

"If I am forced to return to my homeland and to my former occupation of mariner, marriage would mean taking you away from your loved ones and from the kind of life you know. It would be a terrible blow to your father who has done so much for me. I am sure that you could fit in to my kind of life in any part of the world but, again as a mariner, I would be away from home too much and too often, and you would be much alone among strangers. On the other hand, if I remain with the great fur trading company in this country, it might be possible that we could have a happy home wherever my work might permit. You might have to leave your father for periods of time and then we might be able to visit him, or, who knows, we might be able, if I had a permanent base, to arrange for your father and mother to live near us.

"I have written to my commanding officer, or Chief, at the Bay, asking for advice and information about my relations with my employers. I am hoping that I shall remain employed in this country and, if so, that I could expect to have some kind of reasonable married life that would be fair to my wife. But until I do hear from my Chief, I can not make any decision about anything. Do you understand me, Papeet?"

She nodded her head with a very solemn look on her face. Then

117

in a very low voice she said: "Yes, I understand only too well. Ever since the day you first talked with me, I have been thinking about all the things you have just said to me, and I have even talked about them with my father. I have been waiting with mixed pleasure and dread for you to speak to me as you have just done."

Then, regaining control of her voice and composure, she said earnestly, "If you were to ask me, I would follow you to the ends of the earth, because my heart has room for no man other than you. I am prepared to wait for the Great Spirit to show us the way we must travel through life. I feel sure that the Great Spirit who brought us together will show us the way we may spend the rest of our lives together.

"My father has told me not to worry about leaving him when the time comes. He wants me to follow my heart without worrying about him. He says he would rather miss me and know that I am happy with a good man than to have me with him and know that I am unhappy. I know that he respects you very highly and would be proud to have you as the husband of his favorite daughter. If anything serious should happen to my father or mother they would be looked after by my older sister and her husband. But, Oh! I would like to live where I could see them from time to time!

"I am sure the Great Spirit, who has been so good to us, will continue to be good to us and will prepare a way for us if we only have patience and trust in Him. Let us not speak about this again until you have heard from your Chief. If we talk about it, each time it will be harder for us to stop talking about it, and we might let ourselves be led to take some action that not only we might regret later but it might displease the Great Spirit whose help we need so much. Let us say nothing to each other on this matter until you know definitely what you can or can not do. I will understand what you are thinking, and you will understand what I am thinking, but let us take care never to let our thoughts become spoken words until the Great Spirit so wills it. Do you agree, my beloved?"

Sandy was thinking so seriously about her points of argument that he hardly noticed the term of endearment which he had heard from her lips for the first time.

"Yes," he admitted sadly, "I do agree with every word you have said. I knew you were very intelligent, and wise, but I never before realized how wise a woman you really are. I will do as you suggest and will wait patiently."

Then suddenly realizing the meaning of the last term by which she had addressed him, he added quickly; "I will wait on one condition; that first I may show you how a man and a lass in love in my Highland homeland would bind such a bargain with each other."

Papeet looked at him in surprise as he stood up and held out his hand for her to stand also. He braced himself as best he could, and with his good arm he gently pulled her toward him. Before she could offer any resistance their lips met in a long kiss. Slowly her arms crept up and around his neck as she clasped him tightly to her, and he stood with his one good arm clasped tightly around her.

They never knew how long that first kiss lasted.

They were brought back to earth by laughter of children who were watching them. The children's happy laughter followed them to the door of the dwelling, which they entered with faces forced to calm appearance and under control.

15
THE EXPERIMENTING ANGELS

The third book written by Peyo-Wah-Mit and being a record of what the dream spirit told him about how vegetable life and animal life came to this world.

In due course, the young man—for he was a man now, having fasted and having conversed with his dream spirit—returned to the Sacred Hill. He arrived before sunset and hoped to see the dream spirit that night. Although he prayed all night long, he saw nothing. All the following day and all of the next two days he continued his supplications to the Great Spirit. About the middle of the fourth night, the cavern in the rocks was again illuminated by the wonder light, and the woman dream spirit stood before him.

She sat down beside him and talked with him. Slowly she tested his ability to write and to read the syllabic symbols. "You have done well," she said, at last. "I now desire you to listen carefully to what I am going to say, so that you may remember my words and when you return to your grandfather you can tell him all that I will have told you. Then you must ask your grandfather to help you prepare a small tablet of hammered copper, little larger than the palm of your hand, on which you must cut with the point of a sharp knife the table of syllabic symbols I have taught you. On one side make the symbols and on the other side show the key design which contains all the syllabic symbols."

Peyo-wah-mit promised to do everything within his power to carry out the instructions of the Dream Spirit.

"Now here are some things you should remember," she began. "You know that there are different kinds of things in the world around you. There are things that you can see and feel and can move from place to place, such as a stone or a branch broken from a tree. There are things that you can see and feel but can not move,

120

such as a growing tree. There are things that you can see but can not touch, such as the sun, moon, and the stars. There are things that seem to exist because you can see them but you can not touch them, such as sun-beams, rainbows, northern lights, and shadows. There are things that seem to exist because you can hear them, such as the 'thunder-birds,' and there are things that exist only in your mind, such as thirst for water, hunger for food, or love for your grandfather.

"You are familiar with the rocks, sand, clay and mud which are underneath all vegetable life—things that grow out of the ground but which are attached to the ground by their roots, such as moss, grass, bushes and trees. You know many kinds of animal life, creatures that are not fixed in place but can move about from place to place such as animals, fish, birds and insects.

"You know that human beings are creatures of animal life but with something else in them that makes them different from other animals. You do not know what that 'something else' is? You have been told what a spirit is, but you do not know what it really is. You have seen dreams when you were asleep, but you do not know what dreams are made of or where they come from. You are now listening to a dream spirit, but you do not know what I am made of or where I came from.

"You have a memory, something in your head, which enables you to recall views you have seen and sounds you have heard, and even thoughts you have thought but have not spoken, but you do not know what your memory really is or how it works. Your memory will be very much involved with all the things I shall tell you. To write a record of all the things in your memory would require many books. But how can so much be stored in the head of one man or woman?

"One of the first things you must realize is that there is no limit to size; no limit to the largeness of things in what we look upon as outer space, and no limit to the smallness of things in inner space. You can not imagine, let alone measure, the sizes of things out beyond the sun, nor can you imagine the sizes of things inside the smallest particle of dust you can see.

"The work of building the universe, and new worlds in it, never ceases. Creation is not a thing of the past but is a continuing process of the past, the present, and the future.

"Everything in nature is based on two invisible forces. These are repulsion and attraction, push and pull.

"Every piece of material in the universe, from the very smallest to the very largest, has at its center a source of two forces. One of these forces tends to push things away from that center and the other tends to pull things toward it.

"These forces are invisible and can only be detected by human senses by the way they act on things we can see or feel.

"FOR ME TO TRY TO DESCRIBE THEM TO YOU I SHALL HAVE TO SPEAK IN TERMS OF THINGS YOU KNOW. You know what an arrow is. Now, let us suppose there could be thousands of tiny invisible arrows in the space as small as the palm of your hand; each tiny arrow would have little strength in itself but with so many operating over a large area the arrows would, collectively, have considerable strength.

"If you shoot an arrow it takes a short time for you to place another arrow on your bowstring and to shoot it, but if there were fifty men with bows and arrows near you, each shooting similar arrows one after another as quickly as possible, there would be a continuous stream of arrows.

"It is something like this that happens in nature. There are continuous streams of invisible arrows being shot out from every particle of matter in the universe, from the smallest speck to the largest sun or star.

"If you hold out the back of your hand so that the light from the sun is upon it, you soon feel warmth from the sunshine. Each tiny particle of the skin of your hand is shooting out tiny streams of tiny invisible arrows, but the force behind them is very, very weak compared with the force behind the invisible arrows shot out from the sun in the form of sunshine, but when the invisible arrows from the sun strike against the invisible arrows trying to leave the skin of your hand the two opposing forces generate heat which you can feel. In this case we may call the invisible arrows from the sun the 'force' and the invisible arrows from the skin of your hand the 'resistance' to that 'force.'

"For anything to exist there must be a proper combination of force and resistance to that force. The existence of everything depends upon not force alone but upon force and resistance. For you to have the feeling of warmth on your hand in the sunshine had to be the resistance of the skin of your hand to the invisible force driving the invisible arrows from the sun.

"All these forces and all things in this world and all things in the sky are the work of the Great Spirit and his helpers who are his servants in carrying out his will. No one earthly man could perform the works of the Great Spirit although your grandfather may have taught you to think about the Great Spirit as one very powerful invisible man. You must now realize that the Great Spirit is much more than one earthly man and that he must have many invisible helpers.

"In the invisible world, beyond the visible world of mankind, there are certain entities which we know as *The Experimenting Angels*, or by a shorter word meaning simply *The Experimenters*. These servants of the Great Spirit have much greater powers and intelligence than have any members of mankind.

"Once this world you live on was a fiery burning sun like the one you see on a sunny day. That sun changed gradually into what is now this world, just like a chip of wood in your campfire that becomes burnt out and gradually cools and becomes something quite different from what it was. A cooling, burnt-out sun becomes land and water and air and, with more cooling, over uncountable ages of time, the dust of the earth or land can be turned into such things as vegetable and animal life.

"Once a new world, such as the one we are on, reaches the stage where it is composed of many elements, the Experimenting Angels begin experimenting with "the dust of the earth": the material of which the new world has been made. No two such new worlds are exactly the same in composition of materials and conditions of invisible forces affecting those materials; therefore, much experimenting has to be done before it can be decided just what kinds of vegetable and animal life can exist and reproduce in the special conditions of the new world. Experiments have to be carried out to see what can be done with the materials already there, or to find out what things should be transplanted there from the tens of thousands of other worlds on which life in some form exists.

"These superhuman beings are something between mankind and the Great Spirit. They work for the Great Spirit in *many* worlds in the same general way that human beings work for the Great Spirit in *this* world. They have control over many things over which men have no control but which men may know something about, but they also have control over many things that are totally unknown to human beings.

123

"A man may take wood from certain trees, bark from certain other trees, rootlets from certain trees, and gum from still other trees, and, by the use of his own thinking apparatus and his own hands using man-made tools, can construct a canoe. The man does not know that the Great Spirit is telling him how to do this; he knows only that by so doing he can provide himself and other men with something useful to be used by him, or them, and thereby improve their conditions of living.

"The beaver, by working alone or with the help of other beavers, can do a few things, such as cause a tree to fall down, or transport parts of a tree to a stream where wood and mud and stones can be used to construct a dam to control the flow of water, and can build beaver houses in the pond of water so formed and thereby improve the beaver's conditions of living; but no group of beavers can do many of the things that men, or even one man, can do. This is because the Great Spirit has given different kinds of intelligence and different kinds of powers to two different kinds of animals; the beaver and man.

"Man has certain abilities that the beaver does not have, but beyond man there are certain servants of the Great Spirit that are not earthly animals as are the beavers and mankind, because they are as much beyond intelligent man in abilities as man is beyond the beaver in abilities. They have an inborn urge to improve forms of life in every new world of the universe that is formed.

"These superhuman entities are called Experimenting Angels or Experimenting Spirits or, more often, simply Experimenters. They, with all their powers, are servants of the Great Spirit just as are the human beings. The beaver can see a man but can not talk with him. Man can not see an Experimenting Spirit nor can he talk with one except on rare occasions in a vision.

"The Experimenting Spirits are not gods (although the sacred scriptures of the white men refer to them rather vaguely as the sons of God who married the daughters of men, and fathered children to them) but they are aides and helpers and servants of the Great Spirit.

"They have only some of the powers and abilities of the Great Spirit. Some of them have more abilities and freedom of action than have others, just as you have more abilities and freedom of action, in some ways, than has a beaver, or a trout, or a fish hawk, but each of these three living things can do some things that you can not do.

124

"The Experimenters work first with the formation of crystals, by combinations of elements in the materials of a new world. They next experiment with vegetation. With the aid of crystalization forms and other materials in the 'dust' of the new world, and by their ability to transmit already developed forms of vegetable life from various older worlds to the new one by means of the power of invisible arrows, they can make many different forms of vegetable life appear in the new world.

"The Experimenters know how to design and how to build physical materials into things you can see and feel, things you know as vegetable life; that is, things that have roots of some kind attaching them to the ground, and things that you know as animal life that are not attached to the ground but are free to move about in the air or in the water, such as animals, birds, insects and fish.

"The Experimenters not only design and build these things, much as you and your grandfather might build a teepee or a canoe, but they have the ability to put life into those things—something you could not possibly do with anything you might build.

"When the first Experimenters came to this world they began by making the soil from the dust of the earth and then they made things having vegetable nature and then things having animal nature.

"Some of the things they made here were first designed and made here according to the type of dust and the general conditions the Experimenters found here, but some other things had been first designed and built in other and older worlds. Sometimes these latter things had to be changed somewhat in order to fit better into the conditions of this particular world. Sometimes the Experimenters mixed the old and the new to produce things not known elsewhere. Many things were built here from designs brought here by the Experimenters but some forms of vegetable life or animal life may have been moved from some other world to this world without change.

"When I say that forms of vegetation are moved from one world to another, I do not mean that one object of vegetation can be hurled bodily from one world to another. When happens is something very different. That which travels almost instantaneously from one world to another is not something solid but something like a shadow that travels unseen until it strikes something that causes resistance to it and produces a visible shadow; but in this case, when the shadow arrives at the distant world it does not remain just a shadow; it turns into a material thing that is the exact duplicate or copy of the thing in the first world that cast the shadow.

"All vegetable life and all animal life grows from dust—the finely powdered earth and stone and metal and all solid materials that together make up the world—but there are many different kinds of things in that dust. Not all worlds have the same kinds of things in their dust. The dust of one world may lack certain things existing in the dust of another world. In order to reproduce a vegetable grown in one world and sent to another in shadow form, the world to which it is sent must have the same things in its dust that were in the dust of the world on which the vegetable was grown. Lack of any corresponding thing in the dust of the receiving world would result in defects or changes in the reproduced vegetable, or in no reproduction at all.

"Many things now living in this world have been sent here in this manner. Some are exactly the same as their originals in the world from which they were sent, but some have been changed, more or less, because of differences in the content of the dust of this world, or because of some invisible forces peculiar to this world.

"Some things can be transmitted from one world to another without the aid of specially formed or made receiving material, but some things require that special receiving materials or apparatus must be in position in the receiving world before the transmitted shadow can be caused to materialize or be brought to life.

"You know the difference between a pine tree and a birch tree, but what you do not know is that perhaps one hundred kinds of trees were transported invisibly from some other worlds to this world but failed to materialize or to survive on this earth, before the tree you know as a pine tree was sent here from some far away world in the sky and did take root and thrive and reproduce its kind under the particular conditions of this world.

"Perhaps your pine tree came from a star you have often seen. Perhaps it came from a world far out in space that is invisible to you. Perhaps the pine tree and the birch tree came from the same far away world, or perhaps the pine tree came from one world and the birch tree from another world in the opposite part of the sky.

"Each kind of tree received built-in instructions on how to grow to be its own kind of tree and how to reproduce after its kind, and to pass on those instructions to the next generation.

"Many different kinds of vegetable life were so transplanted in this and every other new world in the Universe, to see which would survive and, of these, which would be weeds and which would be useful for the next higher form of life.

"When a new world became developed to where there were sufficient varieties and quantities of vegetation to support animal life, experimental forms of animal life were transported to it from older worlds. Some of these sent to this world were not suitable for survival here under conditions that changed from time to time. Some forms of animal life were of the highest forms developed on various other worlds and, from time to time, other forms were transported here by invisible arrows while the Experimenters tried to find which type would be most suitable to be the type of body to contain the next higher form of life.

"Experimental forms were made here on this earth by crossbreeding different species of animal life from other worlds. Some died out but many were allowed to continue to breed in the hope that improving general conditions here might enable them to improve. The more a new world became populated with animal life born on it the less the Experimenters transferred materials from other worlds to it.

"Next after the development of animal life on this world came the spirit of man to live in the body of the highest form of animal life on the earth. This 'spirit of man' could not live on this world until there was a suitable animal body for it to live in. The combination of the man-shaped animal and the spirit of man became the being we know as man, or, collectively, as mankind, human beings.

"The Experimenters who were sent by the Great Spirit to this world were without material form as you know it. Their work was to develop from the materials of the new world, the dust of the earth, a creature that could have material form, could exist in the air of the new world, could remain alive by means of the materials of vegetation, water and air of this world, and could reproduce its kind, generation after generation. Their work was to develop the animal part of the man. Later, other Experimenters in more material forms would be sent from other worlds to implant in the man-animals the invisible something that is a tiny part of the Great Spirit itself. This is something like a talking book that is alive in the head of the man-animal. It is alive only when the body of the man-animal is alive. This is what we call the atshakoo or 'soul' of man, as distinct from the 'body' of man."

The dream spirit paused and asked the young man if he understood what she was saying to him. He admitted that much of it was strange to him but he was sure that with the help of the notes he had written on birch bark he would remember everything she had said, and that he would understand more of it after he had meditated upon it and discussed the matter with his grandfather.

"Now," the dream spirit said, "you must rest and when I return I shall tell you something about how mankind came to this world."

"This is the end of the Third Book written by me; Peyo-wah-mit, grandson of Moosoom."

16
THE FOURTH BOOK OF PEYO-WAH-MIT
Prehistoric mankind and lost arts

THE FOURTH BOOK WRITTEN BY PEYO-WAH-MIT being a record of what the Dream Spirit told him about early man in this world; the product of "The Experimenting Angels."

The young man made careful notes of what he had been told and he then fell asleep. When he awoke from a restful sleep the dream spirit was smiling at him. After a few cheery words of greeting she spoke to him as follows:

"I desire you to write some more notes of what I shall say to you, so that when you return home you will be able to write a detailed record of all the things I shall have told you.

"You know that there is a difference between a man and a beaver. Both have a body but the body of a man has a soul.

"The body of man is visible because it is made from, and is kept alive by, the dust of this earth; but the soul of man is invisible and is not made of things from the dust of the earth. It is a small part of the Great Spirit; a much smaller part than is contained in an Experimenter, but to a very small degree, a live human being is an Experimenter, insofar as this world is concerned. The early Experimenters worked with the materials available to them to produce the man-animal. Members of mankind now have the duty to use all materials available to them to produce things to better the conditions of mankind in general.

"The human *body* is something like a canoe, and the human *soul* is something like a man sitting in the canoe and able to paddle it from place to place. With a paddle, the man in the canoe can cause it to move about as he wills. He can use the canoe to serve his purpose in many ways. So long as the canoe is in good state of repair and in working order, the man can move it where he wills on the water, but if the canoe falls apart or, being overloaded, sinks in the water the man can no longer stay in it. If the canoe dies, sinks, the man can not live on or in the water without it and he dies also.

"In somewhat the same way, while the body of a man is alive the soul of man in it can move it about by controlling the body, but if the body of the man-animal dies, the soul of that man has no earthly place in which to live. Being a servant of the Great Spirit, it returns to rejoin the Great Spirit to serve in ways no man could possibly understand.

"The animal body of a man is really more like a canoe carrying two men than like a canoe carrying only one man; the abilities of one man being confined to moving the canoe about and making use of it, with the abilities and duties of the other man being confined to keeping the canoe in repair and in good working order. I have already told you that the controller of the actions of the human body of man is called the soul of man. I now tell you that the repairer of the body of man is called the *life* of man. Thus, the man consists of three things: *body, life,* and *soul.*

"Without the soul, the body may live on, but merely as an animal body. With out the life, the body dies and the soul can no longer control it or remain in it. While the body is alive, the soul has a little, but very little, control over the life of the body, but it can co-operate with the life in some things or it can oppose some of the work of the life in the body. The controller of the body's actions can help to protect the healing of a wound or the repairing of a broken bone but only the repairer of the body, its life can heal the wound or repair the broken bone.

"Actually, all human beings are part human and part Experimenter. Some have much less of the spirit of the Experimenter in them than have others. Human beings as they now exist on this earth are the result of the marriage of the invisible and formless Experimenters and the female animals of the highest type that the Experimenters developed to survive under the conditions of this particular world.

"In the traditions of some peoples living today there is a story that when the animals in the form of man began to multiply on the face of the earth and daughters were born to them, 'The Sons of the Great Spirit' (the Experimenters) looked upon the daughters of the man-animals as suitable to be mothers of their children; children who would be able to live in animal form in the air of this world and to grow and produce children of their own. They took many of these daughters of men as wives, and these wives brought into the world the new beings with much greater intelligence and powers than were possessed by the fathers and the brothers of the daughters of man, but with much less intelligence and powers than those possessed by their fathers, the Experimenting Angels.

"In time, these part man-animal and part Experimenter creatures became the kind of man, or mankind, that exists on this earth today. While most of these members of mankind obeyed the commands of the Great Spirit not to adulterate the new race by interbreeding with man-animal forms of lesser intelligence, or with defective members of their own type, some men did interbreed with some of the all-animal types of man, but the resulting creatures were so different from the best types resulting from the half man-animal-Experimenter-spirit combination that did not interbreed with anything but the best of their own kind, that the Great Spirit decided that enough experimenting had been done. Some good earth beings had been produced but some no-good beings had been produced. The Great Spirit, in its wisdom, destroyed nearly all the man-like creatures that were not of the best type that resulted from the intermarriage of 'the daughters of men and the sons of the Great Spirit.'

"It is that part of 'Experimenter spirit' in you that makes you, and your fellow men, different from the other animals of this world who do not have any inherited strain of Experimenter spirit in them.

"As you grow older, and learn more about the white men from the lands toward the rising sun, you will find that some white men believe that the intermarriage of 'the sons of the Great Spirit' and 'the daughters of men' was a great sin, and that punishment for it is a curse or spell that continues to be handed down to all men. This is a great mistake. The only 'sin' for which men must suffer is the 'sin of ignorance'; ignorance of the need to work constantly for and with the Great Spirit.

"Mankind, as a species of animal life on this earth, is not the result of sin but is the result of successful efforts of the Great Spirit to produce an animal body that could, on this particular world, provide a home or dwelling place for part of the spirit-being of the Experimenters.

"In their own forms and composition, the free-moving Experimenters could not live long or reproduce their kind in the air, temperature and climate of this world, so they had to have a dwelling place in an animal that could live and reproduce its kind under the conditions of this world. Their experiments with the dust of the earth produced a type of animal that they considered suitable to live in, so they, with the help of the Great Spirit, chose the daughters of men who were pleasing to their eye, and fathered children by them. As I have said, these children were the ancestors of the species of beings now known as mankind or human beings. You are a member of that species of beings and so have been your ancestors for myriads of generations.

"In other worlds having different conditions of air, water, heat, or cold, and certain invisible forces and things unknown to you, special beings capable of living under those other-world conditions had to be developed before the spirit of the Experimenters could be combined with them to produce a superior type of being for each particular world. For this reason, it would seem to you that the highest form of beings on one such world may live only in bitter cold, or, on another world, only in extreme heat, or, in another world they can live only in water, and in still another world can live only in dense smoke or in burning flame.

"In such worlds, your earthly form could not live in its unprotected form. Each inhabited world has its own type of superior being living on it. Relatively few have, as their superior beings, anything with the apparent same form and composition as the being on this earth called *man*, but the beings in some of the worlds of flame, bitter cold, or vile vapors may be far superior to man in intelligence and abilities to make use of the material things *of his own world*. Just as on this world, the Great Spirit is experimenting with them and is expecting them to work to improve themselves and the conditions effecting their lives in their worlds.

"The first members of mankind on this world had straight black hair, white skin and hazel-colored eyes. After many generations of living in the sunshine, the skin became tanned and more dull, copper-colored than white and their eyes became more brown or black. But some of the first race of men lived in parts of the world where there were always clouds and little bright sunshine. Their skin became pinkish white and their eyes became blue or gray, and many had hair more blond that black.

"Then from an older world came a still more intelligent type of human being, men and women with long wavy red hair, and whitish or pinkish skin speckled with brownish spots wherever it was exposed to the sun. These people, being from a very old race, had inherited memories that the first earthmen did not have. They also had vast stores of knowledge on how to make use of materials on this earth, and they had control of many invisible powers totally unknown to the earlier men of this world.

"Some of these men took as their wives the fairest daughters of the first men of the earth and had many children by them. In time, their children with the wavy red hair, freckled skin, and bluish green eyes became the dominant race on earth. They were the men with knowledge and skill to do things by having the black-haired and the fair-haired races work for them. As time went on, they spread over almost the whole world, on all sides of the oceans and on islands in the oceans. To the dark-haired and the fair-haired people these early red-haired men appeared as being much more than human and they were considered by many to be gods; meaning beings that were in possession of invisible or spiritual powers not possessed by other people on the earth.

"The sons and grandsons of these 'gods' never forgot that they came from a homeland far out in the sky. They tried to devise some way to communicate with their old homeland, or some way to travel to it. They knew that matter could be transmitted from one world to another by some form of invisible arrows but they did not have any of the required machinery or apparatus. Over the ages they kept trying to build the machinery necessary for communication with their old home-world. In time, they succeeded in being able to communicate back and forth with the people of their former home-world. They were told how to construct a receiving station for the transmission to them of some relatively heavy machinery. They spent much time in searching for the proper materials and they forced the other races of men to work for them; as much work was involved in finding and preparing the various materials.

"Before they were able to construct a suitable receiver, the population had grown and consisted of mixed races from the interbreeding of the black-haired, the blond-haired, and the red-haired people. These mixed-race people were, in many cases, the servants or the slaves of the all-red-haired race, and, in some places, rebelled against the latter.

"The red-haired race had succeeded in drawing down power from the sun with which they hoped to establish travel between this world and the world from which their ancestors came. Before they were able to do this, however, there was a serious rebellion and the power from the sun was used against the people who were rebelling. This misuse of the power from the sun to kill human beings greatly displeased the Great Spirit, and the great blast of power that was turned against the rebels was allowed to set fire to the rocks under the land, and the whole great island on which the red-haired people lived went up in smoke or sank out of sight in the sea. The only survivors were people of the mixed races who were in parts of the world far away from where the great fire took place; they and a few of the red-haired people who were on large canoes far from their homes.

"Most of the surviving people did not have as much intelligence or knowledge as did the wise men of the red-haired race but they had inherited memories from which they gradually recovered much of the knowledge that had been lost, but this was a very slow process. Often disease, or catastrophe over which mankind had no control, killed off the men with information before they could pass it on effectively to others. Gradually the human beings that now live on this earth have been improving their scale of civilization and regaining some of the information and powers of their ancestors. Perhaps some day they may become as competent to handle physical matters as were the scientists of the ancient civilization—if they do not repeat history and blow themselves off the face of the earth in another misuse of the Great Spirit's powers."

Peyo-wah-mit had listened attentively to the words of the dream spirit. He now asked the question, "Does the fact that my sister had reddish hair when she was young mean that she is descended from the red-haired people of ancient times?"

"Yes," replied the dream spirit, "she and you are descended from those people who lived long ago on this earth, but you are also descended from other races on the earth, particularly the straight black-haired race that intermarried with the descendants of the

134

first, wavy red-haired people. However, you have also had an infusion of fresh blood from the red-haired people in relatively recent times. That came about in the way I will now describe to you.

"In due course of time, there was in this land quite a large group of people whose ancestors had survived when their homeland sank into the ocean. They had to start all over again to rebuild a civilization with very little except fading memories to work with, because practically all their material possessions had been lost. They had practically no tools or metal to use in making tools, so they had to begin a stone age state of existence. Their descendants succeeded in keeping alive and, in time, developed primitive tools and equipment used in the course of their daily lives.

"The members of this large group that I have just mentioned were mostly people of the straight black-haired type with brownish colored skin. Of course, some of their ancestors had been of the red-haired race by intermarriage before the great submersion of the land, but the people of the black-haired race so far outnumbered the red-haired people that, in time, it was only on very rare occasions that a red-haired person would be seen. There was a time on this world when certain intelligent beings from another world spent some time here. The inhabitants of this world, who saw them, called them the 'Serpent People' or 'Serpents' because when they flew up into the air from the ground they left serpent-like trails of smoke or cloud in the sky. These Serpent People could travel in the air in what would seem to you to be a sort of covered canoe that went up into the air leaving long serpents of smoke that came out of the lower end of the canoe.

"Some of these people married earth women and had children by them; children who were taught many of the secret powers of the 'Serpents.' The visits to this world ceased long ago, but for many years the wisest people were believed to be the descendants of the 'Flying Serpent People.' Eventually these descendants became absorbed into the human race and were more or less forgotten, but some of them continue to carry on as medicine men of various types.

"Ages ago there were people of this world who had much more extensive knowledge of nature and of material things and of mechanical things than have any men of your world today.

"The skillful men of the past had control of unseen forces

unknown to men of today or of the past several thousand years. At some time in the future, all this should again be known to men of your world, but not in your time nor in the time of your grandchildren's grandchildren.

"One unseen force that will first, and to a very limited extent, become under partial control of human beings is that force which results in what you see in the form of lightning flashes. Men will regain knowledge of how to make some uses of this invisible force long before they learn what it really is.

"Another unseen force is that which causes heavy objects held in the hand to drop to the ground if the hand is pulled away and there is nothing visible to support the object.

"If you hold a stone in your hand and release it, and remove your hand, the stone does not remain in the air where you leave it. It drops to the ground, you say. But why should it drop? It moves toward the ground because an unseen force pulls it there. If you could control that force you could make that stone remain wherever you placed it in the air, or you could cause it to move away from the ground, or you could use part of that force to move the stone in any direction you so desired.

"The men of the old red-haired race of the past *had*, and the man of the future *should some day have*, the ability to harness that unseen force so that it might be controlled not only to reduce the pull toward the ground but to move large and heavy materials in any desired direction. Your ancestors of the long dead past knew the secrets of this invisible force and used it for many things.

"Among other things, they made use of this force in connection with large metal structures containing human beings that could travel not only to the moon and back but to some of the morning and evening stars as well.

"Unfortunately, sometimes one of these metal structures became disabled or out of control far away from this world and, instead of returning to this world, went drifting helplessly in space. The people in it died and the structure became their floating tomb wandering through space for perhaps tens of thousands of years before it again came under the influence of the unseen force of this world which could pull it down to the ground.

"Perhaps you have seen a 'falling star' moving rapidly through the sky, sometimes leaving a trail of sparks as it fell toward the earth. Perhaps what you saw was one of those long lost metal tombs

136

of men of long ago returning to earth at such high speed that it melted into many pieces, some of which might fall to the ground and later be found. Such pieces of metal have been found by your people, and by other people who thought the metal must have come from some other world or that it simply 'grew' in the sky.

"Little do modern men realize that such metal was once worked by human hands and was lost in the sky ages ago and was wandering for centuries before returning to the world from whence it came.

"Another unseen force of this world is that which causes variations in the clouds in the sky, with resulting storms and periods of clear sky and bright sunshine by day and clear starlight by night. This force is not uniform in all places on the earth as is the force that pulls stones and other solid objects to the ground if not supported.

"This force varies in strength at different times and in different parts of the surface of the earth. It has little effect on things that you can see other than shell-ice before a storm but you can often hear its effects on ice of lakes in the winter when the ice moans and groans and cracks hours before the approach of a storm.

"This variable force, strong in one large area and weak in another, and always on the move—generally from west to east— effects the air in the sky and in some places pulls down large masses of air somewhat similar to the way the other forces I have mentioned would pull down the stone you left unsupported in the air.

"The changes in the pull or push on the air results in changes of weather. Your highly intelligent ancestors of long ago knew how to detect the variations in this force and that enabled them to know in advance where and when there would be changes in the weather and just where storm areas would travel across the country.

"This strange force that effects changes in the weather is not exactly the same force that pulls to the ground the stone released from your hand or which pulls water downward in streams.

"At some time in the future, as at other times and places in the past, the strange invisible power that pulls water downward will be converted by mankind to something like the powers of the lightning you see in the sky, but this will be under man's control, and will be transported invisibly along long lines of metal to far places where it will be changed again into still other forms of invisible power and made to serve useful purposes for the benefit of mankind.

"Also, still later, when members of mankind remember more of the lost arts and sciences of the past, they will recall how to draw from the very cold regions of this world a warm, dark-colored liquid that can not safely be transported bodily over frozen ground or through ice-filled bodies of water, but which will be used near its points of withdrawal from the bowels of the earth to generate another form of invisible power. It would be useless for me to try to describe all this to you, except to say in simple words that the strange power of the earth liquid would be changed into concentrated streams of invisible arrows that would be shot into the air, from gigantic bows, and aimed at quivers or reception baskets far, far away, where the invisible arrows would be collected and converted into forms of power under the control of man and to be used to expand and improve the living conditions of mankind.

"But, more important, mankind will in time remember how to draw down power directly from the sun and how to convert it into invisible arrows that can be concentrated and directed to recovery-basket-like structures where it can be distributed to many users to provide light and heat and power to move or activate mechanical things you can not even imagine could exist. All these things must be used *only for the benefit of mankind*. This must be remembered at all times, because it was by the abuse of these powers in the past that brought such destruction to this once highly civilized world. Power directly from the sun* must be used by mankind for the benefit of mankind but must not be used to destroy groups of mankind or the resources upon which mankind depends for existence.

"This is all I shall tell you at this time. I shall leave you for a little while and when I return I will tell you something about the way men and women receive help from the Great Spirit."

"This is the end of the Fourth Book written by me, Peyo-wah-mit, grandson of Moosoom."

---

*Could the "power directly from the sun" refer to possible networks of systems of utilizing sunshine in a sufficient number of "sunny regions" of the world to supply constant electrical power to spite of times when some such places would have no sunshine because of night or regular rainy seasons or shorter storm periods?

17
THE FIFTH BOOK OF PEYO-WAH-MIT
The Great Spirit and the stars

The fifth book written by Peyo-Wah-Mit in which is recorded the words of the dream spirit telling about some of the ways mankind is helped by the Great Spirit.

When the dream spirit returned, she said:

"The mind of every mature man or woman contains vast store-houses of tiny things like books of pictures and stories and general information. Also, there are two kinds of memories. One kind is that which you make yourself and is a record of things experienced by your own senses in your own life. The other kind is made up of records of experiences in the lives of your ancestors and which came to you as 'inherited memories' before you were born.

"Inherited memories are things about which modern men know very little, so I shall not expect you to understand me when I say to you that I come to you from your inherited memories. I shall tell you more about this subject before I leave you, but first I must speak of some things that involve your own memory and intelligence.

"In the sky, during the day, you can see the sun and sometimes the moon, and sometimes a star, but at night you can see untold numbers of stars. On a bright sunny day you can hold out your hand in sunshine and feel something from the sun warming your hand. That is because from the sun come untold numbers of tiny invisible arrows. As they strike your hand, the power behind them tries to push them into your hand and you have the feeling of warmth, just as invisible arrows from the flame of a fire make you feel warm. You feel no such tiny arrows when you hold your hand in the light from the moon or in the light from the stars, but every object in the sky that you can see, and many that you can not see, is shooting some kind of tiny arrows in your direction. Some of these tiny invisible arrows become visible if they strike directly into your eye or if they strike some material that reflects them into your eye, such as when you see the sun or the moon reflected from the surface of a pool of water.

"The existence of these tiny arrows becomes known to you only because you have, built into your body, certain things that are sensitive to them. You have two such detecting 'senses' for the heat-making arrows from the sun; your eyes or sense of sight, and your skin or sense of feeling. Actually, you have many other smaller detecting or receiving mechanisms that you know nothing about, and there are myriads of tiny invisible arrows, of many different kinds and from many different sources, that you know nothing about, striking you day and night and affecting your body and your mind.

"These tiny invisible arrows are at once the servants of the Great Spirit and part of the Great Spirit. No matter what you may, in your own mind, imagine the Great Spirit to be, it can only be a dream picture, because no human being and no spirit being, such as I, can ever have the intelligence even to imagine what the Great Spirit looks like. All you need to know is that the Great Spirit exists and helps those beings who help it to help them. The Great Spirit helps those people most who help themselves and one another. Just as each tiny invisible arrow is a servant of the Great Spirit so is each human being a servant of the Great Spirit, and each human being has a duty to perform for the Great Spirit. That duty is to help the Great Spirit in its work of continuing creation by doing everything possible to fulfill the command of the Great Spirit, which is: 'improve and expand.'

"Actually, continuous streams of special kinds of invisible arrows are striking this world from tens of thousands of stars and other worlds in the sky. Some streams of arrows are relatively strong and some are relatively weak, and many are very weak, but the angles at which these invisible arrows meet at any certain point have great influence and effect upon any new life started at that point at that moment. The angles of intersection of the streams of invisible arrows are constantly and rapidly changing, so a life started at one instant would have quite different combinations of angles from a life started, at the same point, even a few hundred heartbeats later.

140

"This applies particularly to human beings. When the life of a child is started, by the union of male sperm and a female egg, the angles of intersection of invisible arrow streams from the many objects in the sky determine what kind of body and mind the child will have, and what will be his natural tendencies, or strength or weaknesses of character, and so on. This general life-plan of a human being is determined by the positions of the stars, the moon, and the sun, at that instant, the instant of conception. The human being will have freedom to wander from the life-plan he is born with, and he will have control to correct some of his weaknesses but, in general, he will follow the life-plan in his natural abilities and tendencies.

"Every human being is equipped with a built-in spiritual clock or measurer of time. This does not keep the time of the sun or the moon but keeps the time of the fixed stars which form the great sky clock.

"The life-plan of each and every human being, when once set up, is not something that changes from day to day without any overall plan or design. The design for each person's individual life-plan is determined according to the instant when the life of that person begins—at the moment of conception. At that instant the spiritual clock in the body of the person begins to function and to keep time with the master clock in the sky.

"On a clear night you can see countless numbers of stars which, as far as you can see, never change their positions in relation to each other. They are the 'Fixed Stars.' There are other bright spots in the sky which are slowly but constantly changing their positions in relation to the fixed stars. The brightest of these is the sun. The next is the moon. The others are the morning and the evening stars, which are the 'Wandering Stars.'

"You know the difference between north, south, east and west, in a general sense. There are two lines of direction that are all important in your life: One is the imaginary line on earth which runs exactly north and south through the point where your life began. The other is the imaginary line of places in the sky exactly over that line on the earth. This may be called your 'Sky-life-line.' A very important point on that sky-life-line is the zenith, the point directly above the place where conception occurred.

"Your life-plan is determined by the sky lights that were on your

141

sky-life-line at the instant of your conception and by the lengths of time, as measured by your built-in spiritual clock (and the great sky clock), between the instant of your conception and the next time when each of the wandering stars, the moon and the sun will cross your sky-life-line, and by their distances on your sky-life-line from the zenith or point overhead.

"Once this life-plan is set up it remains for the life of the individual. No other person will have exactly the same life-plan. A life started a few hundred heartbeats sooner or later, or even a short distance north or south, will have the stars in different positions in relation to your sky-life-line and the zenith, and, therefore, will have a different life-plan.

"You measure the time of day, after your fashion, by the distance your sun is from the sky-life-line, the north and south line through the place where you are. When the sun is on that imaginary line in the sky you say it is *apitah-kesekaw*—'half of the day's travel of the sun.' But the length of the day changes from month to month. In some months the days are long, as in summer. In some months the days are much shorter, as in winter, but at all times they keep steadily and slowly changing in length of time.

"The most accurate way of keeping time that your people have known in recent centuries is the count of beats of your heart, but even that is not entirely uniform.

"The master clock of the sky controlled by the fixed stars is very, very accurate. If you could set up two sticks in the line due south of you and watch when any certain fixed star, moving from east to west, crosses the line of the two sticks, you will find that each night it will cross the line some three hundred heart-beats earlier than it did the night before. Thus, for part of the year you will not see that star at all, because of daylight; but if you look again three hundred and sixty-five days after you first saw the star on that line you will find it will appear at exactly the same time as when you first saw it on that line.

"I am telling you all this, not that I expect you to understand it or to make use of this information, but in order that you may record it so that some persons in the future may read your writing and may be helped by the information.

"Many things in the lives of human beings are influenced by the relationship between each individual sky-life-line and the fixed

142

stars, the sun, the moon and the wandering stars and the effects of the invisible arrows from these bright things in the sky on the life-plan that was set up when the life of that human being began.

"These do not control the human life entirely, and in many ways they are only influences; but if a person knows the natural inclinations and tendencies as set up in his life-plan he can profit by knowing how and when they are affected by the invisible arrows from the stars and the sun and the moon.

"When I speak of the 'time when life begins' for a human being I do *not* mean the time when that being is born and takes his or her first breath. I mean the time when the male and female germs of life joined together and started a new life—that is the instant of conception.

"At that instant the time of birth is determined and is set in the life-plan of that new life. Natural birth will take place at the same instant of time on the great sky clock as was the instant of conception; that is, when the fixed stars but not the sun, moon or wandering stars are in exactly same position with relation to the north and south sky-life-line, but on the day or night nearest to *ten* full changes of the moon after the time the life germs joined together and the new life began."

The dream spirit ceased talking and for a few minutes sat silently beside Peyo-wah-mit. Then she asked him if he had any question he would like to ask her. He told her that he would like to know more about inherited memories and about the people who brought his grandfather's Golden Talisman.

Peyo-wah-mit was told that she would leave him for a short time and that when she returned she would tell him more about these things.

"This is the end of the Fifth Book written by me, Peyo-wah-mit, grandson of Moosoom."

18
THE SIXTH BOOK OF PEYO-WAH-MIT
They who brought the Golden Talisman

The sixth book written by Peyo-Wah-Mit in which is recorded things told to him by the dream spirit about inherited memories and about the red-haired visitors to this world who brought the Golden Talisman

When the Dream Spirit returned to Peyo-wah-mit she began to speak:

"Inherited memories are things you can not see. They are things that may be hard for you to understand, but you can see the effects of them in all forms of vegetable and animal life. A spruce tree seed always produces a tree that grows as a spruce tree because the tiny seed contains a store of inherited memories of how it must grow under different conditions. A young spruce tree growing in a dense thicket, with other trees keeping sunshine from it, will be different from one growing in sunshine and not shaded by other trees, but each will still be a spruce tree, because of its store of inherited memories of how to be a spruce tree and not a birch tree.

"A young beaver will grow to be a beaver because its body has in it inherited memories of how to grow to be a beaver and not a rabbit, and its small mind has inherited memories of what to do with its body for the purpose of building dams and beaver houses to live in, and how to mate and how to look after its offsprings. Your grandfather might tell you that the beaver 'acts by instinct' or that the spider knows how to spin its web 'by instinct,' but I tell you that the beaver and the spider and other forms of life know what to do immediately after birth because of inherited memories; that mysterious something which your grandfather knows as instinct.

144

"Some animals have few inherited memories but these are available to them at birth or relatively soon after birth, while with human beings the inherited memories, other than those of the body-building type, are far greater in number but are much slower in making their appearance. Often they appear only dimly and after long concentration and contemplation. Sometimes they appear as flashes of inspiration, often to the amazement of the person to whom they appear.

"Because there is no limit to the smallness of things or the largeness of things, there is no limit to the number of inherited memories that can be stored inside your body. Many 'memory books' from the lives of your ancestors may be so small and so well packed away that you can not, by your own powers, make use of them. When you fast and pray and concentrate your mind on some subject you may be enabled to revive some of those memories that have to do with the subject in which you are interested.

"The higher powers of the Experimenters, in ways that you can not even imagine but which are normal, natural laws in the worlds of the Experimenters, may be of help and advice to you.

"You are looking at and listening to me, and to your physical eyes and ears I appear to be a human being, but actually I am not a human being. You might say, correctly, that I am the inherited memories of myriads of your ancestors, a sort of personification of a combination of pictures and recored voices of past generations of your ancestors, aided by the Great Spirit through the powers of its servants, the Experimenters. Or, you might consider me as being an Experimenter with the ability to bring to life, in your eyes and ears, certain things that were stored in your vast storeroom of inherited ancestral memories while you were in your mother's womb.

"Any attempted explanation of this to you, by me, can be only symbolic, because if I were to explain in detail the natural laws covering this it would involve so many things that you have never heard of that my explaining to you would be like your trying to explain the details of the syllabic system of writing to a beaver. So, look upon me as one of your great- . . . great-grandmothers; as one of your ancient ancestors who has a very long memory and who desires to tell you some of the things she remembers.

"Sometimes the Great Spirit may give a man exceptional ability to draw 'inspiration' from some of his inherited memories. Sometimes the man uses his gift for good, and sometimes the man uses it for evil, and sometimes the use of this gift produces both good and evil. In the past, sometimes the man to whom this gift or power was given used it with such good results that he came to be considered as a much higher servant of the Great Spirit than is mortal man. Sometimes, for relatively long periods of time, as time is measured in this world, such a man became established in the minds of many of the people of his time, or their descendants, as either The Great Spirit himself or as a combination of the Great Spirit and mortal man, but no mortal man could possibly be equal in intelligence or powers to the Great Spirit. There have been times when such a mortal man, with what appeared to his fellow men as being supernatural powers, was a combination of human being and the invisible being of the next higher state of existence—part human and part Experimenter.

"While the red-haired people had been in control, they had established the language you speak, and they had tried hard to teach all people to speak it correctly. To help them to remember how to speak the language, the wise men had established the old world system of writing that I have taught you.

"While some groups of people did continue to speak properly or to speak the language with only relatively small changes, some other groups of people failed to speak properly or went back to some of the other languages they had spoken before the red-haired people established your language as the standard. Some people, living on lands far away from that land that sank beneath the sea, spoke quite different languages. Most of them had whiter skin than the people of this country now have.

"After the survivors of the great catastrophe came to this land, your people continued to speak the language properly and precisely but, as the numbers of people increased, various dialects were developed by groups of people who, through indolence or laziness in the use of their vocal organs, failed to speak the language properly. The use of the written language became lost to many of these groups during the time when the people were all too busy trying to keep alive in a land new to them.

"However, your group of people had succeeded in climbing back, slowly, on the ladder toward their former state of civilization. They had settled in a district of fertile land in the basin of two large rivers and their tributaries, far to the south of where you and your people now live. In that land they developed a fairly high type of civilization and, by cultivating the soil, they were able to produce food and to live happily. They had not been able to develop any of the mechanical equipment used by their ancestors of the older and higher civilization. They built mounds or hills of earth and on these built structures of wood and sun-dried bricks.

"But another catastrophe befell these people, some thirteen thousand years ago. This time it was due to no fault of your people."

"Will you please tell me something about this catastrophe you speak of," asked Peyo-wah-mit, "so that I may tell it to my grandfather. I am sure that he would be very interested to know about it, because he has told me that he has heard various stories and does not know which to believe."

"Yes," agreed the dream spirit, "listen carefully while I speak slowly to you so you can write it down.

"Far, far out in the sky, people still lived on that world whence came your red-haired ancestors. For ages a few people in that distant world had wondered whether there might have been any surviving descendants of the original colony that came from that world and remained on this earth long, long ago. The belief that had been generally accepted in the homeland of the colonists was to the effect that conditions on this earth had changed and had become such that beings of their type could not exist here, so, they simply abandoned it as a barren world not worth trying to revisit.

"All attempts to communicate with this world had ceased ages before some later-day scientists on the red-haired people's world decided to revisit this earth. By means that could only seem to be supernatural to you, these scientists had detected signs of human life in the basin of the two great rivers and an expedition was sent to investigate.

"The expedition was transported in a manner quite different from the manner in which you might be transported in a canoe from one side of a river to the opposite shore.

"Let us suppose that you are on one side of a river and you have a friend on the other side. If the distance is not too great, you might be able to shout to him and tell him to do certain things for you. You might ask him to make a fire or you might ask him to shoot an arrow into the air. The thing that carried your message to him could not be seen and did not become anything other than tiny invisible arrows until they encountered the ear of your friend. Something in his ear received those invisible arrows and changed them into the sound of your voice and thus made known your message to your friend.

"In a somewhat similar but much more complicated way, the scientists of that far off world could transport by invisible means not merely sound, as you did, but they could transport material objects, such as metal or stone, and living materials such as trees, animals or human beings.

"It was by means of this wonderful science that the 'space-transporter' carrying the members of the expedition was sent to this world, in the hope of finding descendants of the 'lost colony.' In addition to a number of human beings, the space-transporter carried supplies of special materials to be used in setting up on this earth a powerful receiving station for converting invisible arrows from their home-world into materials, and for use in transporting members of the expedition back to their homes.

"After the arrival of the expedition near the place where the two great rivers meet and form one great river that flows toward the south, the scientists made careful examination of earth conditions and then made calculations before beginning the construction of the apparatus which would enable them to return to their own world after their work on this world was completed. It was found that certain quantities of two rare materials would be required before their receiving apparatus or their return transportation equipment could be used.

"After gathering information from the local people, and by their own means of detection of one type of required material, two expeditions were organized and sent off to bring back the required materials.

"One of these expeditions was sent toward the rising sun to bring back a rare yellow metal—the metal you know as gold. The other expedition was sent to the cold country, far away to the north, to bring back a heavy black material which would appear to you to be merely heavy black rock.

"Each of these expeditions was manned by a few red-haired people and a much larger number of local people of the black-haired race. The expedition sent to the east was commanded by a red-

148

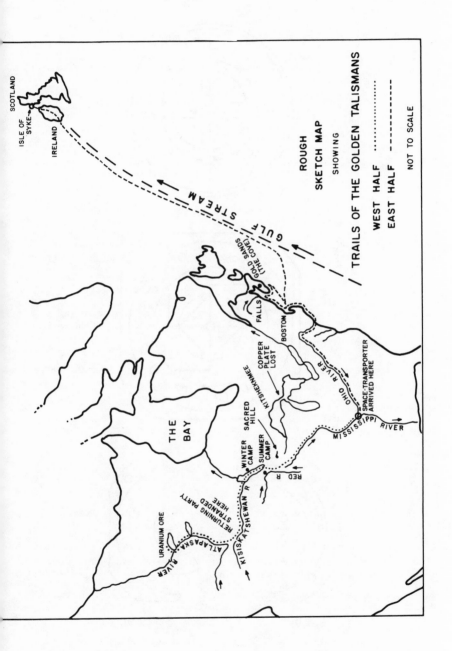

ROUGH
SKETCH MAP
showing

TRAILS OF THE GOLDEN TALISMANS

WEST HALF ················
EAST HALF -------------

NOT TO SCALE

Key to the
phonetic symbols.

Key to the
syllabic symbols.

West Half

East Half

haired man named Kaynook. The expedition sent to the north was headed by his twin sister, whose name was May-koo-stik.

"The twins were the son and daughter of a very famous scientist and they, themselves, were experts in the use of the materials they were sent to procure. They, of course, were familiar with the use of the sound symbols used in writing their ancient language. The brother carried a small metal plate on which was engraved the key to their written language. Before the twins separated to go on their respective expeditions, they cut the metal plate into two pieces and each carried one of the pieces. The part carried by the sister was called the 'west half' and the part carried by the brother was called the 'east half.'

"I shall now show you the designs on both sides of the Golden Talisman as they were before the talisman was cut in two by Kaynook.

"I have already explained to you the markings on one side—the syllabic system of sound symbols. The markings on the other side of the talisman are sound symbols also, but quite different from the syllabic symbols, and they include sounds not used in your language. I shall not explain these symbols to you, as you would have no use for them; but, at a proper time in the future, they may be made known to one of your descendants speaking another language in addition to the one you speak.

"Many records have been written using these sound symbols and, in due course, they may be revealed to future students of the past.

"Now, you must carefully copy these two designs."

Peyo-wah-mit did so, and these are the designs.

When Peyo-wah-mit had completed his copy of the designs the dream spirit examined his work and told him that it was satisfactory.

She then continued her story:

"The original uncut plate was known as The Golden Talisman. It is the west half of that Golden Talisman that is now in the possession of your grandfather. It came to him, down through the ages, from that twin sister; and from the same person came the reddish hair of your own twin sister.

"The two expeditions started out with high hopes and they met with success in finding and collecting the materials they wished to bring back to their friends at the place where they had left the space-transporter. Unfortunately, they never saw those friends again. Although the twin brother and sister lived long lives, they never saw each other again, and, to this day, the two halves of the Golden Talisman had never been brought together.

"Several moons after the departure of the two expeditions, the scientists at the space-transporter began experimenting with their equipment and materials. Because of some miscalculation, they caused a terrific explosion which almost set the earth on fire. Everything was laid waste over an area extending many days journey in all directions from the site of the explosion and this was followed by fires, smoke, and clouds of poisonous dust that made that part of the country uninhabitable for many years.

"Fortunately for them, the members of the two expeditions were far enough away not to be destroyed by the direct effects of this great disaster, but they could not return to their former homes or to the place where the space-transporter had come to this earth from the far away world.

"It was many many generations before the destroyed area of land became once more covered with vegetation, and many more generations before human beings were able to live there. Your branch of the descendants of the red-haired sister's expedition remained to the north of the devastated area and, in time, came to live in that part of the country where you were born."

The dream spirit then said to Peyo-wah-mit:

"Once more I leave you for a little while but I shall return once more, to tell you some things about mankind's duty to the Great Spirit—and to mankind."

When Peyo-wah-mit looked up from his writing, the dream spirit had disappeared.

"This is the end of the Sixth Book written by me, Peyo-wah-mit, grandson of Moosoom."

19
THE SEVENTH BOOK OF PEYO-WAH-MIT
Words of advice for the guidance of mankind

The seventh book written by Peyo-Wah-Mit in which is recorded more of the words of the dream spirit.

When the dream spirit returned to Peyo-wah-mit she began to speak:

"You have been told by your grandfather and others about Kit-shee Manitoo—The Great Spirit. You have heard that the Great Spirit is spoken as 'He' and is something like a man but with strange powers over all things. You now think what you have been taught to think; but now you must think as a man.

"When you become a man you must realize that you must do your own thinking. The Great Spirit gave you a brain with which to think and you will not be doing your duty to the Great Spirit until you use your brain to do your own thinking.

"You can begin to use that brain for thinking about two things in particular—about the Great Spirit and about yourself and how and why the Great Spirit made you what you are today.

"When you begin to really think, you will realize that the Great Spirit is not a man, although you may continue to think of 'Him' as something like a kindly old man of great mysterious powers who will always be your friend so long as you do not do things to offend 'Him,' and even then 'He' will try to guide you to the proper paths of life for you to follow.

"In the language which you speak, the word Manitoo originally meant 'a stranger'—*'not one of the known group of people'*—something having life but not a visible body and, therefore, much like a stranger or unknown person from a strange land but very, very different from any man.

"The word Kitshee meant 'great and powerful.' When the two words were used together, Kitshee Manitoo, they meant 'The Great Unknown Stranger' or the 'Greatest of All Unknown Strangers' or 'The Supreme Unknown Stranger' or simply 'Great Spirit.'

"You do not have the imagination to even think what is the form or the location of the Great Spirit. All you need to know is that the Great Spirit exists and you exist because of the power of the Great Spirit.

"No man should be so foolish and so ignorant as to believe that there is no Great Spirit. Man is only one of the things brought into this world by the Great Spirit who made the grass, the flowers, the trees, the animals, the fish, the insects, the sun, the moon and all the stars. No man, or no group of men, can make a new kind of flower or design and produce a new wing for a butterfly.

"A man can build a canoe by making use of materials provided by the Great Spirit in the form of wood, bark, tree roots and gum from certain trees, but man can not simply look at those materials and say to them 'I command you to become a finished canoe!' The man can only build the canoe by the use of his hands and by the help of his hands.

"In a somewhat similar way, the Great Spirit did not order the dust of the earth to become, suddenly, a spruce tree or a blueberry bush. Just as the man who built a canoe did one thing after another by the aid and the use of his helping hands, so did the Great Spirit make things in this world one after another by the aid and the use of his 'hands' or 'helpers,' which for lack of a better name we can call the Experimenting Angels. These are really the 'hands' of the Great Spirit. You do not need to know what or where they are; all you need to know is that they exist.

"The invisible *life* of the body has its inherited memories of how to keep the body in a state of repair, but it is also capable of receiving 'arrow-borne instructions' that are sent out continuously by servants of the Great Spirit. The *soul* of man but not the physical body of man can hear voices telling it what should or should not be done under any possible combination of circumstances.

"These 'voices' are servants of the Great Spirit and are talking all the time to all men, night and day, giving out advice to human

154

beings on every thing that could possibly happen. For any human being to derive help from these voices he must be able to adjust the 'ears of his soul' to hear only the voice that is talking about the subject in which he is particulary interested. This is not done by physical or body action as much as by action of the mind, in a state of concentration and prayer.

"When a man is born, his soul and his life each has certain built-in ear-like parts that let them hear some of these instructional voices more clearly than other voices, and more clearly at certain times than at other times. Therefore, both the *life* of man the *soul* of man will, at times, hear loud but different voices and will be influenced accordingly. Different human beings, therefore, will hear different inner voices and, in following their instructions, the result is that no two human beings are exactly alike in either material form of the body and its day-to-day growth and repair, or in the mental characteristics as evidenced by the actions of the soul in controlling the actions of the body.

"The difference between a wise man and an unwise man is that the wise man's soul hears more, and heeds more, of the instructions from the Great Spirit than does the unwise man. The wise man continually prays to the Great Spirit for wisdom, which is merely the ability to pick out the inner voices giving instructions on the things he should or should not do. The unwise man hears only faintly or partially the voices of instruction and often ignores what he does hear.

"Some individual persons and some groups of people appear to work against the best interests and wishes of the Great Spirit. Their resistive actions are often the experiment which, in the long run, enables other and better people to survive. They exist for a relatively short time and then disappear or revert to some minor position when they have served, or have failed to serve, the purpose of the Great Spirit in furthering improvement and expansion.

"The Experimenters have always had much more knowledge, power, ability, and wisdom than have the members of mankind.

"The inborn urge of mankind to learn more and more about everything sometimes causes men to exceed the limits of their wisdom and to start things that go far beyond their power to control.

"When men were set free upon this world to make use of all the things established, before their arrival, by the Experimenters, they were given dominion over all those things that had been produced and given life by the Great Spirit through the activities of His Experimenters. But it was emphatically made clear to mankind that there were certain things they must not experiment with, and they must not let the intoxication of their spurts of increase in knowledge tempt them to try to 'make use of the fruit of the tree of life' to experiment with things involving the 'life' of material things.

"Man was told that he could make use of the fruits of all of the trees of knowledge except the tree of life; that man was free to make use of many kinds of knowledge for dealing with material things of mineral nature, vegetable nature, and animal nature, but mankind was forbidden to make use of any knowledge tending to implant life in any of the things made by mankind from mineral, vegetable, or animal materials.

"Mankind was given freedom to endeavor to observe and to learn everything possible about life, as it exists, and how to protect it, and how to limit it, for the good of mankind, but was definitely forbidden to try to add life or the 'fruits of the tree of life' to any material thing not already endowed with life, or to attempt to implant human intelligence in any other form of animal life. This prohibition included giving life to any being, possible monster, or other thing that might be produced by man's forced crossbreeding of forms of animal life.

"If some members of mankind should defy these instructions and attempt to add the fruits of the tree of life to their material productions it should be the duty of the other members of mankind to prevent such action and to chastise, if necessary, by death, the disobedient members of mankind, because the prohibited actions of a few might lead to the destruction of very, very many.

"Also, mankind was forbidden to interfere unduly with the 'life of the world' or the routine things of nature which control and operate such things as the tides, day and night, the seasons, the weather and the methodical behavior of things in the sky, such as the sun, the moon and the stars.

"Far back in the past, a form of beings on this world became so intoxicated from partaking of the fruits of the tree of knowledge that they, in their self-confidence, self-righteousness and ignorance of what might be the results of their actions, so upset the routine movements of this world in relation to the sun that the whole sky appeared to spin around; and when the clouds finally cleared away, the sun appeared to rise in the wrong direction and to set in the wrong direction. Enormous bodies of water rushed over the land and washed down hills and mountains. Over widespread areas, the valleys were buried under great depths of soil carried by the rushing waters. In other places, the bottoms of deep bodies of water became dry land. All this caused great destruction of vegetable and animal life. Mankind was driven back almost to its early animal form and had to start its upward climb all over again.

"I have told you of the invisible arrows and you must know that there must be some invisible but powerful force propelling each such arrow.

"The invisible arrows exist in uncountable numbers and are so exceedingly small that enormous quantities of them may be contained in any small piece of material. If the force of an uncountable number of such arrows could be sufficiently controlled to be directed all in one direction and all activated to operate at exactly the same instant of time, even if for only one infinitesimally short instant of time, the result would be something like the explosion of gunpowder in a gun but would be an uncountable number of times more powerful and more destructive, and, if in the hands of misguided members of mankind, could be used to interfere not only with the 'life of mankind' but with the 'life of the world.' It is to prevent such interference with 'life' that the Great Spirit has set these prohibitions.

"The Great Spirit desires all dominant races on a world to learn all that may be possible to learn about the natural materials and forces surrounding them. It is His desire that those materials and forces be used freely and fully for the general benefit of all inhabitants of that world but not for selfish benefits to a few or where harm may be done to other beings.

"On this world, as well as on other worlds, there have been occasions when a few members of a temporarily dominant race of beings learned how to have some limited control over the concentrated actions of the forces behind the invisible arrows and used them with lack of wisdom and, thereby, upset the routine movements of nature and caused the obliteration of nearly all of their fellow beings.

"At other times, a few members of a dominant race of beings have attempted to make use of the forces behind the invisible arrows not only to entertain, inform and advise their fellow beings at great distances from one another, but to forcibly corrupt and to control the thinking of great masses of their fellow beings, thus causing the latter to ignore and to disobey the wishes and the orders of the Great Spirit. This eventually caused the Great Spirit to reject and to discard that race of being as useless for His purposes in improving the living conditions of intelligent beings on that world.

"All this may happen on this world if too many members of mankind allow a relatively few of their fellow members to play too far with the fruits of the tree of knowledge and use them for the selfish benefit of one small faction of mankind without due regard to the rights of, or the possible danger to, the greater numbers of mankind. If this is allowed by mankind to go too far against the orders of the Great Spirit, it will mean the end of the present form of mankind as the dominant race of beings on this world.

"In addition to those people descended from only the children of 'the Sons of the Great Spirit and the Daughters of Men,' such as the men of your race, there have been some people in this world having various different forms, skin coloring, mental powers, and social behavior that were the results of crossbreeding between inferior members of the 'good' race of mankind with visitors from other worlds, or beings brought or sent here from other worlds by means of invisible arrows.

"Some of the descendants of the mixed breeds obeyed the commands of the Great Spirit to 'improve' but some others did not obey the commands; they ignored them or did the exact opposite. Instead of helping to improve conditions of living for mankind they did much harm, and opposed those who were trying to make improvements. Sometimes this was done deliberately with crafty misuse of intelligence, but sometimes this was not so much evil intent as it was lack of intelligence; and still greater lack of wisdom.

"Some such people still live. The Great Spirit gives these people a chance to improve themselves and to become useful to the human race as a whole, but, when it becomes apparent to the Great Spirit that such people are a menace to mankind, and a menace to the work of the Great Spirit, whether they comprise a small group or a whole nation, or a group of nations, they are discarded as unsuccessful experiments, and they fade away and forever die as important groups or nations.

"Sometimes, a few evil people, disobedient to the laws of man as well as to the laws of the Great Spirit, can destroy a whole nation. The Great Spirit gives to mankind in general freedom of action to police itself; that is, to protect itself from evil-doers by taking direct action upon such evil-doers to cause them to cease their evil-doing. If the evil-doers are allowed by their fellow men to continue their evil-doing without hindrance or punishment, the fellow men of the evil-doers are failing to do their duty to the Great Spirit and, in time, will suffer punishment for their lack of proper prevention of the evil-doing. The Great Spirit has made it abundantly clear that *any nation that can not police itself need not expect to long endure upon this or any other world.*"

After a pause the dream spirit said: "Now, this is the end of my visits with you for this time. I am pleased with you for what you have done, so far, and for your intelligent interest in the things I have told you. I shall leave you. You will go to sleep and when you wake you will partake of nourishment, and after some rest you will begin your journey back to the home of your grandfather. With his assistance and advice you will make a record of all that I have said to you during this visit to the Sacred Hill.

"May you always remember the things I have told you, and may you always have the wisdom to be guided by those ever present instructions of the Great Spirit.

"Until our next meeting! Good-by."

The light went out. The dream spirit was no longer there. The young man was soon asleep.

"This is the end of the Seventh Book written by me, Peyo-wah-mit, grandson of Moosoom."

20
SANDY ARGUES FOR PERMISSION TO PUBLISH THE BOOKS

After reading the Books of Peyo-wah-mit, there was much discussion by Sandy, Kesee Pay and Papeet about what should be done about making known to others the contents of the books.

"I believe," insisted Sandy, "that the contents of these books should be made known to the world. They indicate possibilities that should upset many of the current theories held by white men about the way vegetation, animal life, and mankind came into being, and what happened in the unknown times before recorded history began."

"And how would you propose to make those 'possibilities' known?" inquired Kesee Pay.

"By having them published in my native land," answered the Scot.

"Do you really think you could find many readers who would believe them to be anything other than childish tales or fantastic dreams told for mere amusement? Do you think that any grown man in your country would do anything but laugh or sneer at any book claimed to have been written by what your people call 'an American savage'?" asked Kesee Pay.

"Yes, of course," replied Sandy, but with less confidence in his voice. "Scientists are always trying to find out more and more about the past. The Books of Peyo-wah-mit should provide new ideas to think about and to try to confirm or refute."

"My friend," began the medicine man in a serious tone of voice, "I do not pretend to know about the minds of men in your homeland but I do know a little about some traits of human nature in this part of the world, and what little I have heard about men who come to this land from across the great salt water indicates to me that some of their traits of human nature are not so very different from ours. Unless I am greatly mistaken, you would not find it so easy as you think to arouse any serious interest in these books in the minds of your countrymen. First of all, how would you find any makers of books willing to go to the expense of producing for you the books translated into your language? Even if you could afford to pay a book maker to print the books in your language, where would you find readers to give any serious thought to the texts or contents of the writings of the Indian, Peyo-wah-mit? Perhaps a few might be interested, in moments of relaxation, in reading the books while thinking them to be nothing but utter fantasy or 'fairy tales.'

"You know," he continued, "that in our language we have many 'fairy tales' that are repeated over and over for the temporary amusement of people of all ages, but no person gives any serious thought about there being any truth in them. I know, and I think you know, that these Books of Peyo-wah-mit are not mere fairy tales written and told for the amusement of children or unthinking adults; but, it is my belief that you would have difficulty in finding any book maker who would produce the books in your country, and there would be still greater difficulty in interesting people to give any serious thought to their contents."

"Perhaps you are right," admitted Sandy. "Nevertheless, I would like to try to have the books printed in my country. I would hope that they might stimulate interest among some of the older families to search through their relics of the past for the missing half of the Golden Talisman, which I feel sure must be somewhere in Scotland or Ireland."

"Your motives are good, but, first of all," pointed out Kesee Pay, "I must remind you that the Books of Peyo-wah-mit are in my custody. No person may see them without my permission. You have seen and heard what is written in the books, by my special permission, but you could not make a written translation into any other language without the assistance of myself or my daughter—even with my permission. At this time, I do not know any reason why I should give you permission. On the other hand, I can think of several reasons why I should withhold such permission."

"Surely," said Sandy earnestly, "you will not withhold permission for me to try to write an English translation of the books, when you know how much I am interested in them and how highly I value their contents."

"You may value their contents," smiled Kesee Pay, "but why do you think that any other white man might give serious thought to them?"

Without hesitation Sandy replied, "There are at least two very important things that should be helpful to the white man's civilization of the present day. One is the whole series of strange and unorthodox ideas about prehistorical happenings on this earth that should stimulate and encourage original thinking. Another thing is the general idea of a system of writing based on very simple sound symbols in different positions, each position representing one sound and one sound only. One of the greatest afflictions of each and every language of Europe is the lack of a simple but accurate system of representing consistently the many sounds of a language. The system of sound symbols described and used in the books of Peyo-wah-mit may be ideal for your language, since its sounds are relatively few, but would be of very limited value in writing English or any other European language because the languages of Europe all make use of many additional sounds not used in your tongue. Nevertheless, I feel sure that the principle of such a system of simple sound symbols could be worked out and used to advantage in printing books, newspapers, etc., in English; perhaps not for script or handwriting but for use on the printed page where reading would be made so much easier by the use of simple characters with various positions of orientation."

"Very well," agreed Kesee Pay, "for the sake of argument, let us assume that I give you permission to produce an English translation of the books. What would then happen?"

"I should immediately begin to work on it," Sandy replied.

"You might barely get started when you might receive orders to return to your base on The Bay where we could no longer help you, or you might be sent back to your homeland as, so you have told us, may well be what the future has in store for you. Your only hope to be able to complete a translation of the books would be if you remained in this country where we, or at least my daughter, would be near you in order to help you. But what chance could you have to do that, unless," he added with a smile as he glanced at the girl, "unless you should decide to marry my daughter and remain with us!"

"You may think you are joking, my father," beamed the girl quickly, "but the joke might be on you if he married your daughter and she went with him."

162

"Oh! Ho!" laughed her father, "Now why didn't I think of that!"

But Sandy was not laughing. He was grimly in earnest when he said, "If my prayers are answered and I am to remain in this country for some time, that which has been spoken as a joke may well have a chance to become a reality, but until I know more about my future I can only hope."

Papeet, with her eyes shining, brought the conversation back to the subject of the books. "Have you any other reason," she asked her father, "why the contents of the Books of Peyo-wah-mit should not be made known?"

"Perhaps the most important reason of all," said her father seriously, "is to be found in the text of one of the books. We must not make known the system of writing until the time foretold in the books. From what I have heard of the sacred writings of the white men, great stress was often placed on the idea 'in order that the Scriptures might be fulfilled.' The same principle must be applied here."

"But where," asked Sandy quickly, "is there any forecast of the time when the system of writing would be made known?"

"We must look it up to make sure," replied Kesee Pay, "but, if I remember correctly, the dream spirit stated to Peyo-wah-mit that the system of writing 'can not be revived and brought into the common use of your people for approximately another two hundred years, although some of your descendants will make good use of it in less than half that time.' Two of his descendants, Papeet and myself, are now making use of it within the time foretold but we must realize that there are still more than one hundred and ten years to go before it will be two hundred years after this information was given to Peyo-wah-mit. At that time it will be revealed by 'Brother Tshim.' We must not do anything to interfere with what he is to do, 'in order that the Scriptures may be fulfilled.' This is my definite decision on the matter."

Sandy could not hide his disappointment. "Is there any good reason," he asked, "why we could not prepare an English translation of the books under a mutual agreement that both the Nayheyawayoo and the English versions would be kept in your custody, and the custody of your successors, until, say, at least one hundred and twenty years from this time?"

"Why do you ask that?" responded the older man.

"Because," replied Sandy, "even if I can not make known to the

163

world the contents of the Books of Peyo-wah-mit I would like to have the honor of helping to make a translation that should, in time, be made known to the world in general and to my countrymen in particular. And there is another thing that seems to me to be very important. The dream spirit told Peyo-wah-mit that somewhere in this world are many written records of prehistorical times that at some time in the future will be revealed to mankind and many may be written in the system of symbols shown on the reverse side of the Golden Talisman. We know the sound values of the syllabic symbols on one side of the talisman but we have no idea of the sound values of the symbols or markings on the other side. Peyo-wah-mit was told that at some time in the future this would be made known to mankind by revelation to one of his descendants. I think that all the information we have now, including the forms of the unknown symbols on the reverse side of the Golden Talisman from outer space in the sky, should be made known so that if the old records written in that unknown system are found they may, in time, be transcribed and translated as have been the information and instructions dictated by the dream spirit and recorded by Peyo-wah-mit by use of the syllabic system of writing."

The old man paused before he made reply. "That," he agreed, "is a matter to which I will give very careful consideration. At this moment, I think it might be possible; in fact, it might be advisable, to do as you suggest."

"Then let us hope that the Higher Power will not send me back to Scotland this year," said Sandy fervently as he looked fondly at Papeet.

21
CONCLUSION

About noon on the twentieth day of February in the year 1726 there was excitement in the village of the Nayheyawayoo Indians where Sandy MacDonald was wintering. Some boys on a bluff looking out over the ice of the lake near the mouth of the river had seen, in the distance, a party of men traveling with dogtrains, approaching from the north and apparently following the shore line of the lake.

The boys rushed to the village to warn their elders, as it was not known whether the strangers were friends or foes. The chief hastily called for all able-bodied men in camp to arm themselves and to prepare an ambush for the strangers as they would approach the mouth of the river. He stated that he was reasonably sure that the strangers must be friendly or they would not be coming so openly in broad daylight but, on the other hand, it would be foolish to take any chances.

The ambush was set, but it did not take long to determine that the approaching travelers were not enemies. On the leading toboggan they could see a flag on a short staff. As it came a little closer they noticed that it was the same kind of flag as that which had been carried by the friendly white man Mis-see-nay-kaw, or "Big Sandy," when he arrived at their encampment at the fork of the Red River. In fact, he was the man who first identified it. He and the Indians on the shore ran out on the ice and shouted loudly to the approaching men, who answered with every show of excitement and pleasure.

There was much chatter from both sides when it was realized that two of the six strangers were men who had been with Big Sandy when he arrived at the Red River in the previous summer. These men said that they had been sent by the great company on "The Bay" to carry messages to the big white man whom they had last seen stretched out on a bed with his arm and leg in splints and bandages. They rejoiced to see him on his feet again, and apparently in good health. They told him that everything was going well at "The Bay" but the officer in charge had sent them with important messages for him, and with some supplies and equipment. Big Sandy was handed a package of letters in a waterproof parchment bag.

On being assured that there was no emergency, and that the arriving Indians did not expect him to return with them, Sandy made no attempt to read his letters until after the men had been escorted to the village in the shelter of the spruce trees and had been well supplied with food.

After the excitement had quieted down somewhat, he withdrew from the excited crowd and sat down beside the fire in the center of the winter lodge which he shared with the medicine man and his family.

Without betraying on her face the anxiety which she felt about the new turn of affairs, Papeet, without saying a word, heaped more fuel on the fire to give the white man more light to enable him to read the papers he had received; and, while he sat reading, she sat silently across the fire from him with her father, and from time to time she added more material to the fire.

Sandy had sorted out his mail; two personal letters from relatives in Scotland, one letter in a man's hand from London, and two letters from his commanding officer at the Company headquarters on the Bay. One of the latter, the smaller, was marked "Personal and Confidential." The first one he opened was from his sister, back home on the Isle of Skye. It gave news of relatives and a few bits of local gossip but there was nothing of excitement or news of importance in the letter As an apparent afterthought, his sister had added a postscript: "Give my best wishes to my black-haired, brown-faced sister-in-law—whoever she is! Ha! Ha!" This brought a smile to the face of the white man as he looked quickly across the fire and caught Papeet's eyes watching him intently, but she dropped her eyes quickly and nothing on her face showed that she had seen his smile—or that she was worried that his letter was from some old girl friend of his on the other side of the great salt ocean, and that memories of that far away white girl might have brought that happy smile to his face.

He laid that letter aside and picked up the larger official letter from the Company headquarters at the Bay. He opened it and read a rather lengthy statement of facts; that there was great regret that he had been forced by severe wounds to remain in the interior of the country, and hopes were expressed that the man delivering the letter would find him in good health and in good spirts. He was told that his canoe men had returned to the Bay without any major incident. They had made inquiries, as they traveled, about the possibilities of finding supplies of fish for dog feed if an overland trip on snowshoes and with dog-drawn toboggans should be attempted. In view of the developments as given in more detail in the letter marked "Personal," it had been decided not to wait until the ice went out in the spring before getting in communication with him, and, therefore, the Indians were being sent with information to prepare him for what was hoped to be done in the spring. Fairly detailed instructions were given to him about meeting the canoes carrying supplies that would be sent to him in the spring, if he confirmed that he could meet those canoes at the portage between Pimitshikamee Lake and Deep Water Lake at the head of Muskaseeya River, etc.

Without waiting to read further, Big Sandy picked up and opened the letter marked "Personal and Confidential." After a few opening words of greeting and well wishing, he read:

"It has been decided in London that your 'Agreement of Association' with the Company is to be renewed and that, under my direction, you are to be placed in charge of the exploration and mapping of the interior. As this involves all lands having drainage into Hudson's Bay, it has been assumed in London that this will require several years of your time, at least. Provision has been made for you *and your family, if any,* to be based at this House, or to be supplied from here, as may be required by you from time to time.

"I must point out to you that the Governor and Gentlemen in London have not yet agreed to the suggestions of myself and some others that we establish additional trading posts away from the coast, because some of the Gentlemen of the Company feel that there is no need for us to go to that expense so long as the natives will come to us with their fur; but, at last, there appears to be general agreement that we should obtain, for study and future reference, all possible information about the people, the animals and the geography of our domain.

"In particular, I am directed to explore, and to map in detail, all possible known routes of travel and all possible alternative routes. This work, of course, I must delegate to you and I know you will carry it out with discretion and efficiency and, therefore, I shall not hamper you with any detailed instructions, except for a suggestion relative to your return route.

"Your suggestions for your proposed operations in the summer of 1726 and the following winter meet with my approval and you are hereby authorized and instructed to carry out those operations; but, if it can be conveniently arranged, I would suggest that when you return to the Bay, in the summer of 1727, you travel by the stream draining the waters of Lake Winnepik into Hudson's Bay and, insofar as possible, make a detailed survey of it. We know that some Indians from the interior must come to the Bay by this stream but we really know little about it."

Sandy MacDonald read and re-read this letter with a great deal of satisfaction. Here were the answers to the questions that had been troubling him for months. His future was assured, for several years at least. He would be relatively free to move about and to learn more about the great land in which he had become so interested, and, above all other things, there was the happy realization that now there was no logical reason why he could not marry and become a family man.

Both Papeet and her father had been sitting quietly watching Sandy while he read his letters. They could see by his face that the news evidently was not bad. When Sandy suddenly jumped to his feet and strode with outstretched arms toward Papeet, she sensed what was to come and arose starry-eyed to meet him.

He clasped his arms around her as he solemnly and fervently said: "I love you, Papeet. Will you be my wife?"

Her father, who sat with a satisfied smile on his face, could barely hear her happy, low-voiced reply:

"Tapway pikwaney, seyakehittan, kakeekay iskoo kakeekay."
"Yes, most certainly, Oh my loved one, until the end of time."

22
EPILOGUE

In due course, Sandy and Papeet were married, and he returned to work with the great fur trading company.

Both were very much interested in the things they had learned from the Books of Peyo-Wah-mit, and at every opportunity they collected all possible information from Indian Medicine-Men. Sandy learned how to use what the Indians called, "Inherited Ancestral Memories," but which English speaking people often referred to as "Spirit Writing" or "Automatic Writing."

Like many of the employees of the great fur trading company, some of the children of Sandy and Papeet were sent back to Scotland for schooling. Some of those children would later return to North America, but some would remain in Scotland and marry Clansmen there.

Sandy wrote much material including what he had learned before he was married and in the years after his marriage. His eldest son and their first two daughters were sent to Scotland to live with Sandy's sister and family. The boy eventually returned to the fur trading companies' territory. Both girls remained in Scotland and eventually married Scottish men.

Sandy had hoped to write a book, but died before this could be completed. From time to time he had sent pages of manuscript to his eldest daughter, in Scotland, to be retained until he could be retired and could return to his old home to do his writing.

A descendant of Sandy and Papeet, born in 1892, was able to make use of much of the information Sandy had written, and he arranged for the publishing of a book bearing the title, *The Golden Talisman and The Experimenters*. He had hopes to write a sequel which would include more information about the markings on the Golden Talisman, but he in turn lost his eyesight and his sequel had to be reduced to one subject. That subject was the ancient alphabet as used on one side of the Golden Talisman. What he wrote about it is as follows:

"Over one thousand years ago Arabic scholars gave the Western world a simplified system of symbols to represent numerals. The system was so simple and so logical that it was adopted by writers of many languages regardless of the local names and sounds used to express the ideas represented by the symbols.

At least in the English language, these numbers are known as "Arabic Numerals." They represent ideas internationally understood. They do not represent sounds, but it would be a great help to International understanding if a somewhat similar system representing speech sounds common to most languages could be used by all nations to simplify their own systems of printing their languages and to make easier the understanding of other languages. If all would use the same system of symbols to represent speech-sounds, just as they now use the system of Arabic numerals to represent numbers, it would simplify the entire system.

The copyright was merely for record purposes. I seek no monetary return for the use of this system. All I wish for is to see it put into use.

The country that would first put this system into use, and thus set an example for the rest of the world to follow, could be sure that its name would go down in history in that connection.

Ever since printing with moveable type came into use many men have attempted to introduce improvements in the forms of letters used.

These men were motivated by two basic desires. One was to improve the readability of the printed letters. The other was to develop some system of phonetic symbols to represent sounds of speech that would amend or replace the deficiencies of conventional spelling.

One of the earliest known English thinkers to write about phonetic problems in a systematic way was John Hart, who died in 1574 A.D. He was, apparently, more interested in making better use of the letters of the alphabet then in use than in designing new letters, but he did design several symbols to be added to that alphabet.

Hart made a detailed analysis of speech sounds and the actions of the vocal organs involved in producing them.

John Wilkins, who lived from 1616 to 1672, carried the analysis farther and presented not only a phonetic alphabet but described a system of shorthand and made a series of drawings showing relative positions of parts of vocal organs when speech-sounds are produced.

Beginning in the 1840's, two Englishmen, Isaac Pitman and A. J. Ellis, carried on extensive efforts to design and to put into use a system for printing words of the English language based on phonetics.

Pitman developed his system of shorthand, based on a phonetic analysis of speech-sounds. After this, he turned his attention to the development of a printable form for his phonetic system. He and Ellis worked at the design of a "phonotypic alphabet" to take the place of the conventional English alphabet then in use in printing books and newspapers.

Apparently, the chief aim of Pitman and Ellis was an educational one; the replacement of the inconsistent and confusing system of ordinary spelling with a phonetic alphabet which would help reduce the then prevailing illiteracy among English speaking people.

They stressed the importance of an alphabet that would facilitate learning by reading. One of their expressed aims was to produce *"a system which shall be much more easy to read than to write."* The general idea being that letters printed from metallic type would be uniform in appearance and would not vary in shape and size as would letters produced by the free-hand actions of different writers. *Such printed letters, or speech-sound symbols, should be so designed as to reduce eye-strain to a minimum.*

Pitman and Ellis spent much time and money in their attempts to introduce journals printed with their system of symbols to represent sounds of the English language. Many of their symbols were those of the ordinary English alphabet; some were modifications of Latin and Greek letters, and some were invented symbols. Among the names given to this system of sound symbols were: "The Phonetic Alphabet" and "The Phonotype Alphabet."

The expressed goal of Pitman and Ellis was the substitution

of their phonetic alphabet for the conventional alphabet then in use. They met with strong opposition from newspapers and churches. However, they accepted the opposition as part of the historical struggle of printing against vested interests. They believed that the chief opposition of the newspapers was the cost that would be involved in procuring and using new type, and that the opposition of the churches was based on the growing knowledge that it was printing that had enabled humanity to detect religious despotism and free itself from ignorance.

The purpose of this essay is to deal with the problem of a system "WHICH SHALL BE MUCH MORE EASY TO READ THAN TO WRITE," because the "writing" would be done by "typing" or "printing" with the use of metallic type.

I propose, for serious consideration, something entirely different from the conventional alphabet but which could be adopted to replace it; or to supplement it, at first. My system is based on very few basic forms of symbols, but those forms are increased in value by three basic grades of orientation— horizontal, vertical, and mid-way between those two positions. On a printed page these grades or degrees of orientation are very unlikely to be confused.

Basically, the only lines involved are:

A short straight line.

A short straight line about one third of the length of the former.

A curved line being approximately one quarter of a circle.

A curved line being one half of a much smaller circle. There is a dot, which when attached to a line representing an "unvoiced" sound, indicates the "voiced" sound nearest to the former; such as the difference between P and B.

Other speech-sounds are represented by the way the short straight line is joined to a long straight line or to another short straight line, and by the stage of orientation of these combined lines.

Curved lines are not combined with straight lines, except some half circles.

Certain other speech-sounds are indicated by the stage of orientation of the unmarked chord joining the ends of a long curved line, or by the orientation of the unmarked diameter of the small half-circle.

The symbols may be tabulated as follows:

Four straight lines alone.

Four straight lines with attached dots.

Four straight lines with angles at one end, the short line pointing *upward.*

Four straight lines with angles at one end, the short line pointing *downward.*

Four straight lines with two angles at one end.

Four curved lines alone, being quarter circles.

Four curved lines with attached dots.

Four angles of *two* short lines, in four positions.

Two double angles, *four* short lines, in two positions.

Four small half-circles.

Two small half-circles joined, in two positions.

A total of 40 symbols but the horizontal "straight line alone" is used only as hyphen.

The design below shows how the straight lines, curved lines and dots are used and how the resulting consonant symbols are interrelated.

The page that follows shows details of the vowel symbols.

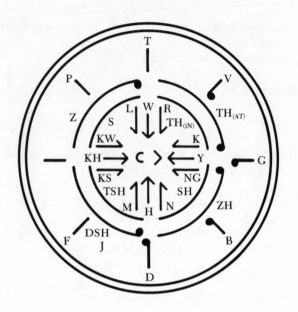

VOWEL SYMBOLS

GO	TOO	ALL	MA	MAY	SEE

COOK	HER	FAT	PUP	TEN	FISH

G<u>O</u> O > GO

C<u>OO</u>K ɔ COOK

T<u>OO</u> OO ʒ TOO

HER ʒ HER

<u>A</u>LL A ↵ ALL

F<u>A</u>T ᴜ FAT

M<u>A</u> AH < MA

P<u>U</u>P C PUP

174

M <u>AY</u> $\overline{\text{AY}}$ ∨ M AY   T E N ◡ T E N
                    ↑ ∨ | ◡ ↾

S <u>EE</u> $\overline{\text{E}}$ ∧ S EE   F I SH ∩ F I SH
                    ⌐ ∧   / ∩ ⌐

CONSONANT
SYMBOLS

It will be noted that, to avoid confusion when symbols are "printed by hand," the short straight lines are joined only to the longer straight lines—not to the curved lines or arcs. Dots are attached to only the *left* end of a straight line or only to the *right* end of a curved line.

The basic essentials are sound common sense and should be easily and quickly learned because they are phonetic and not likely to be confused with any sound symbols of any language currently in use, and *they should make the reading of printed pages easy on the eyes.*

Also, the adoption of this system would provide an opportunity of reforming the spelling of words, because my symbols do not represent letters of the English alphabet, but do represent vocal-organ positions, movements, or sounds which are used in forming certain combinations to represent ideas.

As stated above, the system I propose is not likely to be a source of eye strain. It is intended for use in printing from "type" and, therefore, the angles of orientation would always be uniform—since the main features are either horizontal, vertical, or mid-way between the two—but although my proposed system is intended, primarily, for use in printing from preformed metallic type, including typewriters, there is no reason why it could not be used for freehand "printing."

I call this the LOKHAN system of speech-sound symbols because the original Gaelic sounds of my clan surname can best be represented by the spelling L O K H A N.

It is to be expected that older persons would probably resent any attempt to have newspapers, magazines or books printed in this sort of type, but there is no logical reason why it could not be taught to the younger generations, who should learn this along with the conventional alphabet.

Books printed in the alphabet now in use will continue to be read, because so many of them are in existence, but soon new printing could be done using the symbols I propose.

One logical way to introduce these symbols would be for newspapers or magazines to carry a part of a page printed in this manner, beginning with short items that would interest children. This could be gradually extended to cover more and more material until whole sections or whole books, magazines or newspapers could be printed with this form of type.

The following symbols were made "by hand" and are not nearly as accurate or as regular as they would be if made from metallic type:

/ ← /	as in cold	/ ↑ /	as in hat
/ ⊷ /	as in gold	/ ↓ /	as in water
/ ＼ /	as in pit	/ ← /	as in you
/ ⬳ /	as in bit	/ → /	as in loch, ïch

/ ǀ /	as in teen	/ ٦ /	as in men
/ ٩ /	as in dean	/ ト /	as in hen
/ ╱ /	as in fat	/ ↓ /	as in led
/ ✔ /	as in vat	/ ↳ /	as in red
/ ⌐ /	as in sold	/ → /	as in kwan, quick
/ ❢ /	as in prize	/ ⌐ /	as in tracks, tax
/ ⌐ /	as in thin	/ ← /	as in king
/ ꝺ /	as in that	/ ← /	as in sing
/ ⌡ /	as in show	/ ⌣ /	as in church
/ ꝯ /	as in pleasure	/ ◡ /	as in George, Jane

SYMBOLS USED TO REPRESENT ENGLISH SOUNDS

/ > /	as in note	/ ꜛ /	as in cook
/ < /	as in father	/ ᴄ /	as in but
/ ∨ /	as in fate	/ ◡ /	as in pet
/ ∧ /	as in meet	/ ∩ /	as in pit
/ ⸰ /	as in too	/ 3 /	as in her
/ ⤳ /	as in all	/ ◠ /	as in cat
/ <⸰ /	as in brown	/ ᴄ⸰ /	as in spout
/ <∧ /	as in try, sigh	/ ᴄ∧ /	as in bite, sight
/ >∧ /	as in soil		

LONG VOWEL SYMBOLS ARE POINTED
SHORT VOWEL SYMBOLS ARE CURVED

A DOT AT THE END OF A NON-VOWEL SYMBOL
INDICATES THAT IT IS VOICED

THE L O K H A N SYSTEM
OF
SPEECH-SOUND SYMBOLS

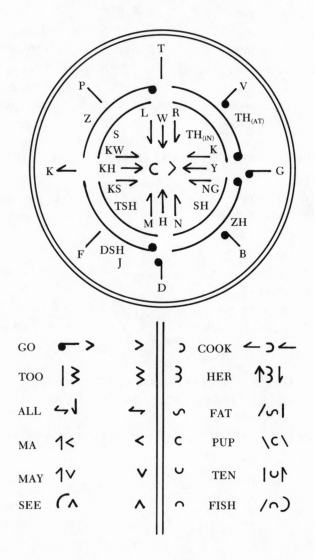

NOTES

1. Site of the city of Winnipeg, Manitoba, Canada.

2. The fur-trading company known as The Hudson's Bay Company, the H.B.C., or "The Bay." It has been in operation since 1668.

3. The Indian name for Lake Superior, meaning "Great Body of Water."

4. Cree term meaning "rapid flowing water"; this river is now known as the Saskatchewan.

5. The pirate ship *Whidah* commanded by Capt. Samuel Bellamy. See Drake, Samuel G., *History and Antiquities of Boston*, 1856, p. 556; and Mass. Hist. Colls., iii, 120.

6. See M. L. Holman, *The Scott Genealogy*, 1919, p. 325, and Gage, *History of Rowley* (Mass.), pp. 169–175.

7. P. Penner and J. McGechaen, *Canadian Reflections: An Anthology of Canadian Prose* (Toronto, Canada: Macmillan, 1964), and Robert A. Logan, *The Precise Speakers*, pp. 284–293.

8. Rev. James Evans, who put into practical use the syllabic system of writing the Cree language five years after his recommendations for its use were rejected by his higher religious authorities. He made no claim that it was an invention of his own, although some later writers made that claim. See his reports in the files of the Library of Victoria University, Toronto, Canada. In 1836 he wrote, in part: "I beg to forward you the following alphabet of the Indian language which by a slight alteration or two is suited to represent the sounds of the Ojibway or Sootu, Kenistino or Cree, the Mushkego, Algonquin, Ottawa and several other tribes scattered from the Rocky Mountains to the shores of the Atlantic." It was not until he was at Norway House, Manitoba, in 1840, that he was free to produce printed material using the syllabic symbols.

9. The junction of the Mississippi and Ohio Rivers.

10. The famous high tides of the Bay of Fundy.

11. The "Reversing Falls" of the St. John River, near the city of St. John, New Brunswick, Canada.

12. The beaches of sand and gold dust at "The Ovens," Lunenburg County, Nova Scotia. See the Report of the Department of Mines of Nova Scotia dated 1929 for the years 1861 and 1862, when gold recovered from the sand weighed over two thousand ounces.

13. Uranium ore country in the Great Slave Lake region of the Canadian North West Territories.

14. Gobi Desert country? The second homeland of the wavy red-haired race—the first highly intelligent human race on earth?

15. The Chipewyan branch of the Athapaskan people, who remained in the north country.

16. Eskimos or Inuits.

17. The Apache-Navaho branch of the Athapaskan people who gradually worked their way southward. See H. Hoijer et al, Linguistic Structures of Native America (Viking, 1946).

18. In the year 1789 a Christie MacDonald married a man in Halifax, Nova Scotia. She had a daughter born in 1792, and a descendant of that daughter was born in 1892. He became much interested in the traditions of his early ancestors which included Highland Scots and North American Indians. With the help of information recorded by more than one ancestor, he received much more information.

   He had the intention of writing a book to include some prehistoric information about a system of sound symbols used by his American Indian ancestors, but because of his time-consuming duties in military services, he was unable to do so until he had served four years on active service in each of two World Wars. He was placed on the Retired list of the Army of the United States. (Note: Not the United

States Army). He became crippled in World War II and is now too blind to see to read or write properly. He is still, however, able to write his own name.